CONTENTS

FOREWORD

WHAT IS YOUR MATHEMATICAL STORY?
—JO BOALER, STANFORD UNIVERSITY

This book is a mathematical story, and it is told by a masterful mathematical storyteller, my friend Sunil Singh. My question for you, as you read my foreword for this book, is: What is your mathematical story?

This is a question I have asked many different people—and I am often surprised, and even more frequently, troubled, by the stories shared. One setting in which I asked this question was the streets of San Francisco, California. I had decided to interview adults about mathematics, to include in my online course for students (called How to Learn Math). I asked the adults, "How do you feel about math?" Then something surprising happened: all of the adults started talking about their performance in math—whether they had been successful or unsuccessful in school. I let the adults share this information and then tried again, asking them what they thought about the subject. The fact that so many adults immediately shared their performance was a clear indication to me that our mathematics approach in schools has sadly been reduced to a *performance subject*. Mathematics is the most overtested, overgraded subject of all school subjects, which causes students to think their goal is not appreciation of the subject but achievement on narrow tests. And those narrow tests have reduced the subject to a set of procedures to memorize and rules to follow. Sadly, many students come to judge their self-worth on their ability to reproduce methods accurately. As the adults shared that day, math in school had provided no room for their own ideas, their creativity, or their imagination. I am hoping that as you think of your math story, there has been and will be plenty of room for all three of those.

Some people in the world have been let in on a secret—a very well-guarded secret—that this performance subject, disliked by so many people, is not real mathematics. And that when students experience real mathematics—a subject that invites them to investigate, wonder, explore, and create—they are often forever changed. As you read the beautiful story that is set out in this book, you will meet students who are introduced to real mathematics in first grade, when Sunil visits their classroom and invites them to wonder about number theory, using cubes to model odd and even numbers and their combinations. The students were enchanted. As Sunil said, they were "overwhelmed by the simplicity, patterns, and beauty of math." I have seen this same enchantment when inviting Stanford undergraduates to experience real mathematics. These undergraduates have often been successful in math classes, but the math they have experienced is one of rules and memorization, and it has left many of them feeling like the subject is not for them. When these students see the beauty of creative, visual mathematics and learn that their ideas matter, and that they get to explore, investigate, struggle, and gain insights, there is no going back for them. This is why Sunil and I, and many of our colleagues, are passionate about introducing a different mathematics to students, their parents and guardians, and anyone else willing to experience it.

As you read this book, you will meet real mathematics—and if you really live the story that Sunil tells, then you will have the opportunity to experience it deeply. I started by asking you: What is your story? Perhaps you are someone who has only experienced performance mathematics or, even worse, been made to doubt your own self-worth because you did not do well in this unappealing subject. If this is your story, this book could be your salvation. Perhaps you are someone, like

Sunil, who teaches mathematics and loves the beauty of real mathematics. If so, this book is going to be a reading treat, as you will be able to enjoy the feast of alluring mathematics. There are many different experiences that may bring you to this book, but whatever they are, I hope they give you the occasion to experience real mathematics, and the wonder and joy—*and wellness*—that accompanies it.

That is the story of mathematics that all of us should experience. *Chasing Rabbits* is a hopeful and timely primer to secure that promise.

INTRODUCTION

The cure for boredom is curiosity.
There is no cure for curiosity.
—Dorothy Parker

24 is a factor of 288.
What a perfectly odd way to start a book. Stating a wholly benign math fact to get your attention. If I can be even more ludicrous, let me state that 24 is also a factor of 24. It's also a factor of 48. If you think I am going to mention 72 or 96 next, you would be wrong. Those numbers are not interesting in *this* mathematical story.

In a couple of sentences involving very accessible mathematics, you should be curious as to what is really going on with 24—colorfully confused is my hope! But why the trivial mentions? Why the unexplained omissions? Combining equal parts *boring clarity* and *cryptic mystery* has created a seductive tension in mathematics for thousands of years—resulting at times in the kind of nonsensical conversations one would find in *Alice in Wonderland*. (I would hope that the linguist-mathematician Lewis Carroll would have approved of my playful silliness!) But there is no nonsense going on here. I have only chosen to come at this cool mathematical idea through a more cloaked path. I could have been direct and less coy, but then we would have lost my personal amusement—and your personal bemusement. Our best math moments often occur when joy intentionally selects confusion as a dance partner. There is one brewing right now. It's a story of quirkiness and playfulness. And, without this pairing of ostensibly strange emotions, we would have lost this story to the sterility of facts and order. Instead, I gave it to the whimsical humanness of narrative (sticky note this right now).

Anyway, 288 isn't the interesting number. The interesting one is its neighbor on the floor above, 289. 25 and 49 are interesting, too. Do you recognize these numbers now? Squares, right! Prime squares. And it's actually even more interesting than that: every prime square (except 4 and 9) minus one equals a number with 24 as a factor. I'll prove this in detail in chapter 8, but in the meantime, what's important to note is that I learned this nifty fact about primes in late 2020, decades into my career as a mathematician and teacher. One can't write a book with *chasing* in the title without subscribing to its delightfully light ethos—the idea that mathematical delights come not only from mucking around between the question and the answer, but from spending as much of our lives in this beautiful, joyful, and life affirming . . . *muck*. This is a major theme of this book. Finding muck. You will find me there. It's my earnest hope that this book guides you there, as well.

Chasing in the world of mathematics is my story of wellness. Our simplest definition of *wellness* is "a state of good health in body and mind through a deliberate effort." Wellness in mathematics for me is quite similar—a purposeful pursuit to find the healthiest ideas of learning the subject. It is an internal smile that mathematics has brought to my life. Very little of it has had to do with finding answers. Most of it has had to do with finding the right questions and then going on miniquests and microadventures with them. Destinations unknown and arrival times uncertain. Not to mistake this mathematical itinerary as cloudy and vague; it's beaming sunshine and deposits of noteworthy color for far as our eyes can see. This book will get you going—but I won't *release you* until the final chapter.

Where do we generally find the most amount of real muck? A forest, right? Which is why I chose for the cover of this book to be a forest. A forest that looks inviting and enchanted. One that symbolizes the beauty of a *mathematical forest*. While this forest is metaphorical, imagining mathematics as such came from spending much time in *real ones*, especially in my childhood. The forest had multiple effects: It was calming. It was mysterious. It was rejuvenating. It was green wellness.

It had paths that varied in their evidence of having been walked upon. The green moss on rocks always intrigued me. Fallen trees and saplings held equal fascination. Forest flowers seemed more special, as they were less likely to be seen than those in manicured gardens. Your shoes were always guaranteed to gather mud. The smell. Ahhh, the smell. Only nature could create an aroma that mixes the living and the dead and feels like therapy in a bottle. The smell of sticky-sweet autumn leaves that have fallen to the moist ground is one of my favorites. This is how I *now* see the world of mathematics. Everything about it can be found in our childhood fascination with forests. We just have to look at mathematics through a lens of kindness, gratitude, and of course, curiosity.

As such, I didn't just open with a math fact. I found this ridiculously small wildflower of mathematical delight while mucking around in one of the thousands of patches in this magical wonderland of numbers, patterns, symmetries, and everlasting truths. There are thousands of wildflowers. The abundance of mathematical blooms is everywhere. This book is a story of my *unfinished* trek through this space. The "24" wildflower, which still hasn't had its petals revealed, had to be my first offering. When we offer flowers, they come with love. How else to begin a book about math than with love for the discipline at its simplest and smallest level—while still invoking a gripping mystery.

The most important words in the title of the book are *mathematical wellness*. And, how we get there is by chasing ideas, problems, conundrums, puzzles, and stories of mathematics with unbridled thirst and curiosity.

It is all about the mathematics. As such, you shouldn't be surprised by how this book began—or by how it will end. Mathematics is everywhere, dancing effortlessly between the abstract and concrete. Our mathematical forest is where all of this takes place. To be honest,

I can't even tell you where in the forest I am or where I am going. But it is precisely this imprecision and uncertainty of my coordinates here that has caused a most piercing sensation of being centered within math. The following 230 pages reveal my journey to this strange, comforting middle. A journey that has seen the value of mathematics increase when it is not separated from the continuum of life. A specific seduction of mathematics has arisen from this understanding—that mathematics has meditative powers. I hope my writing so far gives a glimpse of this.

Embedded in wellness is also the call to rehumanize mathematics. This is also a call to center our own lives with humanness—something that feels increasingly more distant for the mentally, physically, and emotionally taxed classroom teacher. By association, regrettably, are students who only believe that, at some point, mathematics will give them trauma. There is no varnished way to describe the historic toll of unwellness that mathematics has had on them.

We as frontline guardians of education are not as well as we need to be. Wellness isn't an option in our stressed-out lives, but we desperately need the equanimity and balance that make up a life of wellness. The nonprofit Global Wellness Institute (globalwellnessinstitute.org) calls on us all to "reset the world with wellness"—and a *reset* is exactly what math education needs. Unfortunately, for the better part of its history, mainstream education has been rooted in an industrial regimen of dehumanizing checkpoints, performance markers, and production output, keeping an almost impervious, bureaucratic barrier against the holistic change we need.

If you have read my previous books, you will know that I spend a fair amount of time threading together mathematics and its extraordinary ideas to ordinary thoughts, reflections, and insights. We always talk about teaching mathematics across different subjects, considering how the wisdom of different disciplines might inform each other—but what if we let this philosophy sit in our everyday life? Let mathematics marinate in the musings that most of us easily subscribe to. I suppose I should provide an example:

I remember reading *Breakfast of Champions* by Kurt Vonnegut on the subway going to university in the '80s, and laughing so hard underneath my breath that I had to get off a few stops early just to compose myself and get my diaphragm to relax. The part that had me running for the subway doors was about this *fictional sentient alien character the size of a bug that communicates how to stop wars and cure cancers through tap dancing and farts.* My whole body and mind spasmed because of Vonnegut's nutty imagination. Vonnegut's writing has been lauded for decades. But behind his spectacular writing lies a person who has championed silliness, playfulness, and foolishness as soul-developing attributes. There is often a false assumption that the seriousness of one's craft is marked by *only seriousness.* Often a rich foundation of childlike beliefs and intentions drives the narrative. This was embodied by a famous letter Vonnegut wrote to Xavier High School in 2007, when he was asked to visit their school. In lieu of a visit (he was eighty-four at the time), he wrote:

> What I had to say to you, moreover, would not take long, to wit: Practice any art, music, singing, dancing, acting, drawing, painting, sculpting, poetry, fiction, essays, reportage, no matter how well or badly, not to get money and fame, but to experience becoming, to find out what's inside you, to make your soul grow.

My edit to that letter would have been to *add mathematics* to that healthy list of artistic immersions. The only thing that has enriched my life and made my soul grow as much has been music. Math education has toiled so long in the achievement-oriented world that attributing any idea of the growth of one's soul to learning mathematics would be laughed at. Students fight an uphill battle just to positively identify themselves with math. If I don't understand it right away, I am not a math person. *If I don't get good grades, I am not a math person. If I don't take calculus, then I am not a math person. If I am bored, then I am not a math person. If I don't see myself in mathematics, then I am not a math person.* Mathematics doesn't encourage soul growth in school; it is a catalyst to its atrophy. Almost two decades later, the stinging commentary of mathematician Paul Lockhart remains valid:

> If I had to design a mechanism for the express purpose of destroying a child's natural curiosity and love of pattern-making, I couldn't possibly do as good a job as is currently being done—I simply wouldn't have the imagination to come up with the kind of senseless, soul-crushing ideas that constitute contemporary mathematics education.

For far too long, education has forced students to chase the unhealthy narrative that equates an interest in mathematics with achievement and success. But being good at mathematics is so not the point; taking a light interest in it is. Which of these two is more inclusive and healthier for our society: ability or interest? Of course, ideally, it should be both. But where has all the emphasis been placed? Ability is linked to comparison and competition. It also can be void of interest—especially in school. I am sure I could obtain the ability to put IKEA furniture together masterfully. But I have zero interest in obtaining that skill set. In mathematics, if your ability ever eclipses your love for it, then I believe *both* will be doomed. Survival of mathematical ability depends on its playing a *supporting* role for interest. As a society, we don't teach that. We tend to value things we can measure. Have we ever checked in on attitude—and whether that attitude is healthy? No. That's because there is a tacit understanding that math trauma will greet many students, and only deep, pervading negative attitudes will appear. It's a heavy tax teachers pay to teach this subject. It's an even heavier one for students who learn it.

Which brings me squarely to health, and specifically how there has been historical malnourishment in math education regarding anything pointed inward to our relationship with this complex subject.

Commentary on this has rarely been direct or come from the math community. Indirectly, it has often come from the arts—specifically, music.

Many of you—especially if you are baby boomers or Gen Xers—are familiar with Supertramp's "The Logical Song." The song is autobiographical. It is about Roger Hodgson's exile to a school where he exchanged his soul for compliance and practicality. In a 2020 interview about that song, he went even deeper. Sitting on some pastoral hill in the English countryside, he reflected with the clarity and tranquility of his setting:

> It's what is missing in school that is for me the loudest
> thing because we are taught to function outwardly. But we
> are not taught inwardly who we are and what really the
> true purpose of life is. There is very little discussion even
> in school. And, I think for me the natural uniqueness and
> natural awe and wonder, and thirst, enthusiasm, joy of life
> that young children have gets lost and beaten out of them.

Lightness. Such a disarming and buoyant word, but one that can easily be connected to finding the most satisfying, soulful center. Just look at the title of the 1984 book *The Unbearable Lightness of Being.* It's not necessary to go into the book's deep ideas about life's ambiguities and paradoxes. It's enough just to see that "lightness" can be associated with rather transcendent allusions. This is how I envision using this word and connecting it to nurturing an interest in mathematics that is airy and uplifting. Wellness is light. That includes mathematical wellness. So, ideally, I would like you to stop reading right now. Go outside. Try to find some distant green horizon, and let those gentle words of wisdom sit with you. Having an instructive pause is warranted by Hodgson's well-timed and well-crafted reflection. It's a lightly measured call for wellness.

Regrettably, mathematics' only home in education has been of outward functionality for society—get a job, make smart purchasing decisions, and analyze the world. All important things. But where is the inward digestion of mathematics? How can we push mathematics into the slipstream of asking deeper questions about the purpose of life without directing focus inward? Questions that were denied to Hodgson still continue to be denied to millions of students. That's why the regaining of our balance with the world and with ourselves through mathematics cannot be tasked to just our educational institutions. It has to be part of our own to-do lists as humans and teachers so that our students can reap the benefits.

Honestly, we have to stop riding the myth that practicality/application will nurture interest for all students. This is dangerous, as it starts to elbow the less practical ideas—like algebra—to the sidelines. Mathematics begins to mirror the societal expectations of visible contribution. Its intrinsic beauty is auctioned off for nuts, bolts, cogs, and wheels. The imaginative colors of mathematics fade; curiosity suffers a similar fate.

One of the most toxic side effects of education institutions' outward-focused mathematics instruction is math anxiety. We know this terrible syndrome didn't exist before the formalization of education. Frustration, confusion, darkness, incorrectness, and failure did. But, not math anxiety. That is a synthetic, toxic polymer of education. Never mind anxiety being a block to understanding mathematics, it is just such an unhealthy thing for a child to be burdened with. But, as we will discover in this book, anxiety is a late diagnosis of the real problem: alienation.

That's why it's high time to devise a standard for mathematical wellness that explicitly ties into some of the recognizable pillars of general wellness:

Physical: A healthy body through exercise, nutrition, and sleep.
Mental: Engagement with the world through learning, problem solving, and creativity.

Emotional: Being in touch with, aware of, accepting of, and able to express one's feelings (and those of others).

Spiritual: Our search for meaning and purpose in human existence.

Social: Connecting with, interacting with, and contributing to other people and our communities.

Environmental: A healthy physical environment and the awareness of the role we play in bettering our natural environment.

Mathematics study can incorporate every one of these pillars. Even those that might seem more far afield, such as physical and environmental wellness, should be integral to how we teach and learn math. We can encourage high school students, for example, to go outside for a walk if they are stumped on a mathematical idea, as James Tanton, the creator of Exploding Dots and cofounder of The Global Math Project, recommended to his students when he taught high school. Here are his unique thoughts on that:

> I would shock my colleagues by assigning to my students the following task for homework: "Tonight you are to go for a 20-minute walk and *not* think about this problem we are currently stuck on. I am serious! You must go for a walk and not think about this." Invariably students came to the next class reporting having had beautiful flashes of insight that successfully moved the discussion forward.
>
> This is the practice and the art of being a mathematician: embracing the seesawing of the conscious and the unconscious, the frustration and the joy, and the dark haze and the rush of blinding insight.

We can help our students understand that fresh air, leisurely strolls, and surrounding greenery can be critical in promoting a deeper connection and purpose to mathematics. Nature makes us pause and turn inward. Mathematics instinctively follows this direction.

I will detail math's connection to the other four pillars throughout this book, though they won't so much resemble pillars as they will paint blotches that bleed into one another. Wellness should become fully integrated with mathematics, just as mathematics should become fully integrated with everyday life. For me, cherishing mathematics means that the role it plays in my life is indistinguishable from the roles played by music, sports, travel, cooking, baking, writing, film, art, friends, family, and my kids. Metaphorically speaking, I wrote this book in the places where math and wellness come together for me: during an early morning stroll on a quiet beach, at a hearty patio lunch with a best friend, or at a loud, boisterous pub, clanging splashing beer mugs well past the witching hour.

The great mathematician Paul Erdős once said that "mathematics is the only infinite human activity," implying that we will never be able to find out everything there is to know about math. And if we look at math's entire history, drawing on a dazzling diversity of tribes, civilizations, cultures, and races that have explored mathematics, we've got the blueprint to participate in its infinite, wondrous, and mysterious entanglements with boundlessness and fearlessness. The message boils down to this: Be curious. Be creative. Be imaginative. Be hopeful.

Be well.

I hope that this book serves as a modest guide to carry us all in the right direction of wellness. The first chapter, "Highs and Lows," is about the wide range of emotions and life changes that occurred early in my teaching career. It's where I met my mentor, guide, and friend in this amazing life trek. It's where I found my first rabbit holes. It's where I want to anchor our starting point with the duality of being both comfortable and uncomfortable with mathematics—and that all the emotions one can experience in learning this subject can be seen, heard, and honored in this broad domain. This might be a stretch of how we see mathematics, but it is not a stretch of how we experience our lives. The honesty of our lives must guide how we explore mathematics—especially if wellness is the endgame.

Getting lost with mathematics will become an emergent theme. Sure, we don't know where we are, but we are all there. Each chapter after that is a story unto itself but will build on previous chapters to continue to make connections to the soothing and soulful ideas of mathematics. Eventually, and hopefully, you will end up somewhere in this forest. I will see you coming. There will be room on the log that I am sitting on. You made it. Not to the end, but to the beginning. Hence, why the last chapter is called "Go."

If you are reading this book, you are a mathematician. And in the words of Russian mathematician Sofya Kovalevskaya: "It is impossible to be a mathematician without being a poet in soul." Recognizing the poetry in mathematics is one way we move toward wellness. So, let's go chase some rabbits. Tripping and tumbling in our pursuits, dreaming of our adventures, and desiring more mathematics than this fragile life can possibly give us. After all, we are all poets in soul, dreaming of a wellness that we all want and deserve. For a lifetime.

HIGHS AND LOWS

What is life but the sum total of our experiences?
—Andrew Hackett

Most days, I have Lou Gehrig kind of gratitude. This constant feeling of being the *luckiest person in the world*. That blessed reflection is not the result of good minus bad—it is because of good *plus* bad. But you probably don't get the wisdom to "add your lucks" until you've passed that optimistic halfway point in your life—fifty.

Though strangely—or maybe not so strangely—my good luck has had the habit of following some devastating bad luck over the course of my life. You know, when life gives you lemons, you make lemonade, or when one door closes, another one opens. A life's road with just as many icy wipeouts into a ditch as sprawling vistas of summer green. Appropriately, if I owned a lemonade stand, it would be happily sitting near some skid marks on a poorly paved road. Being well.

Everything has been a gift. And, invariably, there are people around you in these moments of grief and joy. One of the pillars of wellness is social. I believe this pillar needs even more attention now. That everything we construct in math education must have—in addition to an internal reflection—a social endpoint. Mathematics must have intrapersonal and interpersonal aspirations.

Yes. My life has been a series of ups and downs, all nestled comfortably in life's clichés, sayings, and saws. And one of the most fortunate events to filter out of this inexplicable combination of life's dice rolls has been a *crumbly*, *stumbly*, and *bumbly* path to a lifetime enchantment with mathematics. In fact, I believe there is no more beautiful path. There is no gilded shortcut. But the path of mathematical bliss is wide and accessible to all. The tricky thing, though, is that the path is kind of a paradoxical journey: *You are never going to arrive*—much like Samuel Beckett's character Godot. Pause. Mathematical wellness is somehow embedded in an endless journey *and* personal setbacks? Yes. But for our purposes, that simply means being a lifelong learner and realizing the best moments with math come with almost life-affirming struggle.

As such, there is no terminus with crates of neatly organized math books and courses at the end. There is no road map. You will be traveling lightly, packing only curiosity. You'll have the exuberance to chase mathematical ideas that zig and zag with the quirkiness of fleet-footed rabbits. It is a game you can play for an hour, a day, a weekend, or your entire teaching career. Or you can allow it to wash over your entire life, with only a mere glimpse of its beauty. It took me twenty-five years to realize this. I am hoping it takes you less.

THE GREAT EMPTY

As I said above, you often need bad luck to get to the good—and the entire trajectory of my career in math education was triggered by one of the worst moments of my life, during my first year teaching high school. In 1997, the year I got married, and five years *after* I graduated from the Faculty of Education at the University of Toronto, I finally got my first full-time job teaching at a high school. I interviewed for the position in August at one of the oldest public high schools in Toronto. It is a beautiful building that looks like a private boarding school one might find tucked into the rolling green of a state like New Hampshire.

In fact, it was the high school used to shoot the wildly successful Netflix series *The Queen's Gambit.*

Even though I had three years of experience teaching at a local community college under my belt, my first high school timetable of teaching subjects was still rather unusual. Not only did I have a senior math course called Finite Mathematics, but I also had a grade 12 gifted physics course. In addition to teaching, I also coached girls' softball and boys' ice hockey. And, a few months later, I joined a group of teachers to pilot an equity project at our school aimed at fostering inclusiveness.

It was an amazing year of, as you should guess, highs and . . . lows. While the school was surrounded by multimillion-dollar homes, just outside were pockets of low-income housing. I would have students in my class who came from the epitome of wealth and privilege, and those who were hanging on to life by a proverbial thread. It was a challenging mosaic of human life that I had to contemplate and reconcile every day. The mathematics I taught was pretty meat and potatoes. I was given course outlines. I followed them. But I believe that this most unique social setting offered much-needed color to my otherwise dry lessons. To be frank, my lesson planning took a backseat to, well, *everything.* One of the few things that could bind the students who wondered when their next vacation was *and* the students who wondered where their next meal was coming from *could have been* the humanity of mathematics. Unfortunately, I didn't have academic clarity on that at the time. It would be decades before that gift came to me . . .

What made the school the most unique was that 50 percent of the school population was adults. While this is probably nonexistent in the US, it wasn't rare in Canada. The percentage breakdown most certainly was, but not the belief that both teenagers and adults could benefit from learning together. Adults who were mostly immigrants. Adults who had children. Adults who sometimes had three jobs. My classrooms were snapshots of life's fighters—with a panoramic lens—capturing all the grief, grit, and strife that one could house in eight hundred square feet.

Unfortunately, the powers that be didn't see the value in continuing such a vital program. In spring of 1998, the government was making drastic and unhealthy cuts to public education. One of those cuts was to free adult education at public high schools. You can do the math here. Losing half the school population would mean losing half of the approximately eighty teaching jobs. And, of course, because of seniority rules, new teachers would be gone first. Just as bad, it meant that these hard-working adults, most first-generation immigrants, would lose their opportunity for free education. Naturally, there was protest. It was big. No, I mean BIG. It was not only the largest strike in Canadian history, but it was also the biggest work stoppage ever in North America. Over one hundred thousand teachers went on strike for two weeks.

I had mixed feelings about the strike. On one hand, I was championing for teacher solidarity, but on the other hand, I was also supporting an antiquated model of seniority that is inherent in every single teacher's union. The cause was worthy to be challenged, just not the institution. Sure, the protest was about job loss, but when the dust settled, I would be gone. In a strange sense, I was literally rooting for my own dismissal. But, like a good foot soldier, I joined the picket line. Feeling the pangs of the financial pressure with a new mortgage to pay and a looming declaration of job redundancy, my frustration spilled out. Spilled out in mathematical logic.

I had estimated that the strike was costing about $14 million per day in teachers' salaries. I made a suggestion to our picket captain that we go back to our classrooms on the last day of the strike, refuse our pay, and donate that sum to the United Way. We would still be protesting. We would have a tangible impact on helping needy Toronto communities. And we would be heavily supported by the public for our selflessness. The picket captain only scoffed at the suggestion, giving me a glare that confirmed my hierarchy in the teaching profession—at the bottom.

Eventually the strike ended. A bitter spring would lead to only a bitter summer. During the last week of school, Jean Goodier, the principal of the school, called each of the forty teachers made redundant into her office individually to say a formal goodbye. Since she was doing it alphabetically, I was near the end. By the time I saw her, she wore a face of emotional exhaustion. The kind words she spoke to me that day were broken by an understandable welling of tears. She gave me some parting advice that I still remember over twenty years later: "Sunil, teach the student. Not the subject."

I held it together for as long as possible once I heard I was losing my job. Several weeks after first learning that I would be unemployed, I came home and broke down, crying inconsolably in my wife's arms. I had encountered my first closing door in my teaching career, and it almost crushed me.

Act 1 was over. It was time for act 2 . . .

PETER RABBIT II

(No, there is no typo with "II." You will meet "I" later.) Late that August, I found out that I had been taken off the redundant list and assigned to teach at a school called Riverdale Collegiate. While I was thankful to be employed for the coming school year, there was still heavy emotional residue from my termination at my first job. I honestly wondered if I would ever have such a professionally and personally satisfying year again. Gifted students in a senior physics class. Immigrants living below the poverty line. Coaching two sports. Presenting on equity with the principal. Having to walk away from it all. It had been my first year teaching high school. How could the next possibly be more emotionally overwhelming? The only thing left could be a singular, poignant moment of fate that would define most of my teaching career for the next decade. Of course . . . it happened.

My new school was just as beautiful as my first school. All the staff seemed nice and welcoming, and the principal, Linda Grieve, felt like a second mother. I wish I could tell you more about what happened next—that figurative opening of the door to my *entire math career*—but I can't recall the specifics beyond what I am going to share with you. In the afternoon of my first day at my new school, I went by the teachers' mailbox area to pick up mail and get acquainted with the staff room. There was a gentleman, fiftyish, collecting his mail in the cramped area, as well. He introduced himself. He had a very pleasant British accent. When I told him my name and the subject area I was teaching, he remarked that he was also a math teacher new to the school. I don't know how or why, but I *immediately* went on a rant about math education, in spite of only having one year of experience in the public school system. It wasn't a long rant, as the tight space wasn't exactly conducive to a more intimate and expansive stripping down. But it was long enough for my fellow colleague to get an earful, and just quietly remark, "Let's keep talking." This person would have been in his right mind to be wary of this unsolicited slice of random math education disfavor, but instead, it was the precise moment our wonderful friendship began.

The person I was talking to was Peter Harrison, the new assistant head of mathematics at my school. He had previously been a math coordinator at the board level and had ended up at Riverdale due to a reconstructing of leadership after the government downsizing. His *annoying* humility would not allow me to see how much of an impact he had on mathematics education during his career until most of it was in the rearview mirror. Short-sighted austerity measures would lead me to a lifetime of prosperity as a math teacher, as I spent my early, formative years under his wing. But, more importantly, it led to my blessed friendship with the person who gifted me the history of mathematics and where to dig deeper—*where to chase rabbits*. But, like a great teacher, he only told me where to look, not what to find. The impact of what I found is romantically catalogued in this book.

Peter's first love was geometry, and as such, it was no surprise he spent quite a bit of time lauding one of his mathematical heroes,

René Descartes. But he also spent an equal amount of time celebrating another geometer, a local one from the University of Toronto (both my and Peter's alma mater), Donald Coxeter. Much to my embarrassment, when Peter first introduced me to him, I had never heard of him. But truth be told, I had not heard of many of the things Peter would share with me during our four years together at that school. In the beginning, admitting so much ignorance was mildly painful. But his wisdom and knowledge went beyond facts. It was the way he conveyed them. Mathematical stories effortlessly knotted with mathematical content. While the braiding was always gentle, there was an energy in his stories that carried an imperative to know more. Our best voices are those we use when we tell stories. Peter always told stories. About his students. About mathematics. About mathematicians. As such, his approach to teaching was firmly embedded in storytelling—decades before it became an emergent theme in math education.

By a year or so later, I would look forward to Peter's nuggets of mathematical gold, constantly panning his brain to learn more and more every day.

However, it is H. M. S. Coxeter, affectionately known as "Donald" (a shortened version of his third name, MacDonald) through whom I have chosen to try and illuminate the whole buoyant and mindful journey that lies ahead for all of us. Coxeter represents the unique and magical intersection of history, music, art, and mathematics. He lived ninety-six years—a wonderfully long life spent extracting as much mathematical insight, revelation, and wisdom as one could.

Learning about Coxeter not only exposed me to a singular mathematical thinker and human—it also revealed the blind spot I'd had before Peter introduced me to him. But that's a key aspect of the *crumbly, stumbly* path I mentioned above—gaining wisdom by learning how much you *don't know*. The blind spots only accumulate as you throw yourself with *reckless abandon* into the mathematical prism (sticky note this as well!). But this isn't a blight on you, me, mathematics, or teaching. It is the simple and honest revelation that we are mortals, and mathematical knowledge is in the pantheon of gods. This shouldn't make us feel small—it should make us feel bigger.

DONALD COXETER

A quiet darkness fell upon the world on April 3, 2003. That was the day Donald Coxeter passed away. The night before, I want to imagine, when he knew his time was coming soon, some fragments of mathematical reflections, amusements, and wonder danced one more time in his magnificent brain. Playing with mathematics requires very few resources beyond one's imagination. As such, even if our bodies go frail with age, mathematics can continue to replenish our spirits. We can't cheat our own mortality, but living within the breathing world of mathematics almost ensures that we won't be abandoned by it at the very end.

Coxeter's contributions to mathematics were so great that his name prefaces many geometric ideas: Coxeter groups, Coxeter diagram, Coxeter complex, Coxeter element, Coxeter graph, Coxeter number, and Coxeter system. Suffice it to say, he discovered a thing or two in the world of geometry. But he gave much more to mathematics than formulas and theorems. For example, around the time of World War II, he was asked by the American government to work as a code breaker. He politely declined, due to both his pacifism and his passion for the elegance of the geometric world.

This decision not to apply his thinking to practical (and destructive) endeavors and to continue his lifetime journey with the beauty of mathematics is central to the idea of wellness—purposeful devotion to the ideals of health. His choice not to outsource his brilliance for militaristic objectives. The purity of his mathematical mind was thankfully impervious to any competitive advantage that the US government yearned for. Mathematics is always first created for its own beauty. How it gets negotiated and sold in society's marketplace is almost always secondary.

Sure, he was a vegetarian and cranked out fifty pushups every day, but there must have been such a surplus of peace and balance in his mind to know that his life's devotion was consumed by the mystery of geometry. His deep mathematical musings—*meditative almost*—did not go unnoticed by the world he impacted and influenced.

The passage below, taken from a justifiably sprawling obituary from the UK's *Telegraph*, published just two days after Coxeter died, exemplifies the gentle and humble wisdom that permeated his entire life: "Despite, or perhaps because of, his appreciation of the aesthetics of mathematics, he never used a calculator or computer and wrote all his papers in pencil so that he could go back and correct them. He travelled to work by bus and could often be seen wandering around the university campus carrying a pineapple, which he used in his classes to illustrate natural symmetry."

In many ways, Coxeter's life's work is like a star in the universe: brilliant and shining on its own, but in the grander scheme of the cosmos—which is the universe of mathematics—dwarfed and humbled.

> ## Many people feel small because they are small and the universe is big. I feel big.
> —Neil deGrasse Tyson

In 2006, a wonderful biography by Siobhan Roberts on the life of Coxeter came out, *King of Infinite Space: Donald Coxeter, the Man Who Saved Geometry*. In a review of Roberts's book, James Gleick wrote, "[Roberts's telling of Coxeter's story] comprehends a whole universe— our universe—of kaleidoscopes and crystals, groups and symmetry, bicycles and snowflakes, music and movement. It is lucid, beautiful, and exalting." The review is full of lush and magical words that get at the spirit of Coxeter's inquiry. Coxeter spent a good deal of his life chasing the complex world of geometry. The grace and equanimity that defined him were definitely the products of his leisurely pursuit of mathematics. Let's take *that leaf* out of his storied life. A leaf that shows that thinking about mathematics in a gentle way from time to time throughout our lives just might be a healthier way than being heavily immersed in it—*without choice*—and to eventually be exhausted by the expectations to perform and succeed. That toll is called *math anxiety*. However, there is a precursor to this condition that has been historically ignored. We will examine this later in the book—I promise! A generational influence lies in Donald Coxeter. Let's study the hell out of him and others who have approached math with such life-affirming beauty and humility.

Around 2010, when I was teaching at my last high school, a supply teacher, older than myself, and I were having a conversation about the golden age of mathematical textbooks, the '60s and '70s. He punctuated our discussion with a wide and confident smile, and this: "After all, we were the children of Coxeter."

I have a collection of math textbooks from the last seventy years. If you want to see the romantic decline of mathematics, just look at the prefaces of textbooks from fifty years ago. They spoke with an infectious enthusiasm that was standard for the times. Here is an excerpt from a 1967 grade 10 textbook that was used in my home province of Ontario. Keep in mind that students would be the intended audience. This feels like the foreword for a tantalizing mystery—which mathematics is!

> Mathematically, we live in stirring times! . . . the general public has begun to realize the secret previously only known to a small coterie of mathematicians, that mathematics is a powerful, fascinating, living subject that actually consists of more than dull routine arithmetic and the rote memorization of geometric theorems.

Sigh. I am so lucky that Peter Harrison sent me down the rabbit hole of Coxeter and an era of mathematics that often seems permanently gone. To know that Coxeter's life anchored a whole generation of teachers who started their careers in the '70s. That when they walked into the classroom, Coxeter walked in with them. However, as I would discover, I actually stared at a portal to him every day—as a teenager.

FULL CIRCLE

One of the rites of passage for many Generation X teenagers was the adorning of what seemed like every inch of wall space in your bedroom with posters. Posters that were a visual summation of everything going on in your life. For me it was music, sports, and "weirdo" art. I had posters of Led Zeppelin, Pink Floyd, the Chicago Blackhawks, the Toronto Blue Jays, and one of those psychedelic prints from the Dutch artist M. C. Escher. Little did I know that I was staring quite closely into the mind of Coxeter. Tessellations of angels and devils that spiraled out to the edge of a circle—infinitely. Two images. Black and white. The rationality of geometry colliding with the symbolism of good and evil. The result is an emotional pull that, for me and for others, puts this piece of art up there with the *Mona Lisa*. Unfortunately, it is not. But I did find an artist in Slovenia, Dejvid Knezevic, who describes himself as a "dotted inker"—his pieces of art can contain up to 150,000 dots—who passionately says otherwise.

In a 2018 blog piece titled "A Case for Escher's 'Angels and Devils,'" he goes into passionate detail about why this piece of art is the greatest work of art—ever. I find it deeply satisfying that an artist is so profoundly drawn to something rich with the geometry that Coxeter lived in for most of his life.

Initially, I only saw the menacing devils. How could you not? One of them is staring right at you above the midpoint of the circle! After a second or two of delay, the white angels pop out. The mathematics that led to this piece of art, entitled *Circle Limit IV*, triggered some mysterious thoughts in my brain. I just didn't have the mathematical chops to fully understand how Escher had created this masterpiece. How did he do it?

For starters, we know that Escher's love and gift for symmetry was heavily influenced by his repeated visits to Alhambra, the Moorish palace in Grenada, Spain. The transference of Eastern and Western ideas has always found its easiest passage in the arts. For Escher, Alhambra was a source of his greatest inspiration, giving not only more discipline to his art, but also more playfulness.

Escher, you see, drew all his work from instinct and an obviously deep understanding of symmetry and patterning. He had no knowledge of trigonometry and logarithms, which his work meticulously re-creates. Sadly, he did not think of himself as a mathematician, even though every fiber of his questioning delightfully underscores the fact that he was, as described in the below excerpt from Doris Schattschneider's "The Mathematical Side of M. C. Escher":

> In Escher's mind, mathematics was what he encountered in schoolwork—symbols, formulas, and textbook problems to solve using prescribed techniques. It didn't occur to him that formulating his own questions and trying to answer them in his own way was doing mathematics.

Art is often influenced by mathematical ideas. More rarely, however, is *mathematics influenced by art*. But that is precisely what happened when two great thinkers, each trying to unravel each other's world to find the magical intersection of mathematics and art, actually met. The fateful meeting between Coxeter and Escher occurred in 1954, when the International Congress of Mathematicians met in Amsterdam (they only meet every four years). In no coincidence, an exhibit of Escher's prints, symmetry drawings, and carved balls was put on display. It was the first time that Escher had serious interaction with the math community, though other mathematicians, like Roger Penrose, also interacted heavily with Escher's work, which was soon to be elevated for its rich mathematics.

Coxeter not only met Escher for the first time, but he also bought prints from the exhibition. A couple of years after the 1954 congress,

Coxeter wrote to Escher to request permission to use some of his regular tiling pictures for his upcoming presidential address to the Royal Society of Canada. Escher agreed, and Coxeter in due course (probably early in 1958) sent him a copy of the finished transcript, after it appeared as an article in the transactions of the Royal Society of Canada. The image was Coxeter's homage to the mathematical artist, Escher, and his *Angels and Devils* drawing.

In 2021, a long-awaited documentary came out profiling the life and work of Escher—*M. C. Escher: Journey to Infinity*. Simple, truthful, and wholly encapsulating. An excerpt from a review of the film by Matt Zoller Seitz at RogerEbert.com reflects the art, math, and poetry that have resonated with millions:

> Escher was a rare artist who managed to combine his influences into something genuinely new. His work is a geometric/mathematical surrealist vision of the objectively perceivable world, but also a subjective interior, evoking ancient Arabic-North African graphics; the Salvador Dali-Pablo Picasso-Georges Braque anti-realist sensibilities of the '20s and '30s, and computer models that would not become popular until decades after Escher's own experiments.

My friend Peter's subtle name drop of Coxeter sent me down my first rabbit hole, illuminating a mathematical world of dazzling detail and color. Once we learn from Coxeter and Escher about the infinite forking paths connecting mathematics to history and art, the journey is endless. And let's not forget music. In 1969, the Rolling Stones released *Through The Past, Darkly (Big Hits, Vol. 2)*. The album cover was shaped like an octagon! I am an audiophile, and I think it is the only time that shape has been depicted on a vinyl cover. While that geometric nod was impressive, Mick Jagger was searching for something more visually tantalizing. You guessed it. He wanted Escher to create a specific piece of art for that album. While Jagger was rejected quite unceremoniously—Escher chided him for addressing him as "Maurits"—the letter he penned to him was admiring and respectful and confirmed they would negotiate a fee if Escher accepted the commission:

> In March or April of this year, we have scheduled our next
> LP record for release, and I am most eager to produce one
> of your works on the cover-sleeve. Would you consider
> designing a "picture" for it or have any unpublished works
> that might be suitable?

Even though Escher rebuked Jagger for the query, the request tells us something about the cultural significance and broad reach of mathematics. While there is obviously no mention of anything specifically mathematical in the letter, Jagger's fondness for Escher's artistic *output* is a direct result of the creative, mathematical *input* (including Coxeter's work) that inspired Escher. It would be shortsighted of us to think of this whole story as just charming in some anecdotal fashion; rather, we can see it as emblematic of the ways we need to recalibrate the cultural currency of mathematics, and, subsequently, our system of math education.

Our current system of math education is devoid of the charm, whimsy, and color that sits in a story about the intersection of a famous mathematician, famous artist, and famous rock star. We need to stretch the canvas of how/where/why mathematics greets us. If one drawing by Escher, laden with mind-blowing mathematics, can make someone proclaim it to be the greatest piece of art ever, then there are thousands of similar proclamations extolling the beauty of mathematics lying in wait. Mathematical wellness is a love for not just math, but for self-care.

But where are we? Certainly not here. More specifically, where are our students? How far are they from a less pressurized environment for learning mathematics? How long can the unchecked and uninterrupted stress of students be sustained without causing irreparable damage? The podium of measured success in mathematics is now shared with full-blown anxiety. This path is unsustainable. This path should never have been considered sustainable. Student stress should never have been seen as an expected result of the journey. If so, we are all on the wrong journey with wrong turns.

If you are over forty, you will fondly remember Bugs Bunny cartoons and his recurring quip, "I knew I should have taken a left at Albuquerque." The first time he said it was in 1945, when he ends up in the Black Forest of Germany. Math education needs to make that kind of left, to get back on the road of humanity and curiosity. We need to write prefaces full of romance and vigor, like we did over fifty years ago. To get back on the road of mathematical wellness. This road, with unwritten chapters, unfamiliar milestones, and unknown terrain is what awaits. Curiosity will shepherd us toward a horizon of deeper meaning and connection. Our journey will contravene so many adopted conventions of learning and teaching mathematics. Our footing will sometimes feel unsure, riddled with an almost unshakable doubt.

This book is all about finding stability in this unstable journey. It's not a contradiction. In fact, it is the very road to a lifetime of mathematical wellness. And part of wellness is letting go of failed ideas that have only served to mechanize mathematics in both instruction and in purpose. While this should sound strikingly odd, creating more white space in our minds will give us clarity to assess the larger landscape of mathematics and throw us into some deeper questions: Where are we? Where are we going? *Why are we going there?* These questions are more to be experienced than to be answered, as some new emotions of confusion, doubt, and uncertainty will be experienced. Though they might be new to us, for the millions of people who explored mathematics prior to formal education, they symbolized the mystery of learning mathematics. So again, we need to let go of the soulless preconceptions we have created about mathematics—which not too surprisingly mirror the values of our society. We will lose our traditional bearings and markers. Performance, correctness, speed, and even mastery will no longer be our North Star. Simple wellness will be. However, it will be a complex journey—not the mathematics so much, but how we need to think about its larger, holistic impact on us and society. We will be lost. But we will be lost together.

Just like we have always been.

READY, SET . . . STOP!

The purpose of art is to stop time.
—Bob Dylan

I know the title of this chapter seems to surf some quasi absurdity reminiscent of all things *Alice in Wonderland*. After all, this whole book is about chasing rabbits, right? Isn't that about hustling and bustling while doing math problems and feverishly exploring the enormousness of the mathematical universe? Vast and deep exploration, yes. Accelerated passage . . . no. The world of mathematics might be as psychedelic as Lewis Carroll's nineteenth-century classic, but our time spent here *must be* the exact opposite of the frenetic pace set by the White Rabbit. While his "I'm late, I'm late! For a very important date!" might be appropriate in our current K to 12 math culture of being overwhelmed, overbooked, overobligated, and just over-everything, mathematical chasing has a much different meaning and velocity outside the stress chamber of most schools.

Mathematics is more akin to the calmness—but purposefulness—of a tortoise's strides. Finding that Sunday stroll is also finding the walk of wellness. Why wouldn't we figuratively apply that leisurely and healthy gait to learning mathematics—which could use some fresh air and a slower pace? Now imagine taking this walk into a forest of tall sequoias, aromatic woodsy scents, familiar—and *unfamiliar*—flowers, breezes both felt and heard, and a constant unfolding of new permutations of these gifts. This whole book of thinking about mathematics is devoted to this walk, catalyzed by that day of rest. Mathematics should not be a burden for our students; it should be a balm. The kind that is also supported by sipping coffee, wandering thoughts, a bit of daydreaming, and maybe a nap or two. When it comes to mathematics, I want to turn the color of "stop" from red to green. That progress of thinking about mathematics in its highest plane is literally linked to shutting it down. To know when to stop. To know how to stop. To know why to stop. To be more specific, it—mathematics—shutting us down. Accept a much slower journey and brace for failure. The entire history of mathematics is about being slow and failing repeatedly. Everyone who ventured into this defeating labyrinth did so willingly. School math has been about speed and success with mandatory entry. Square peg, meet round hole.

How absurd, right? Absurdity is kind of responsible for getting me to this point of linking the pursuit of micromysteries, charming stories, and beautiful problems in mathematics with twenty-first-century wellness ideas. My mathematical life has been, thankfully, absurd.

> # To me, absurdity is the only reality.
> ## —Frank Zappa

Here's another shot of absurdity: *unfortunately*, math came too easily to me. Too easily? Yes, and I hope you noticed what I emphasized in that sentence.

So, let's *stop* and think about that. My easy-breezy experience as a student of mathematics was one of those things that caused a severe delay in seeing it through a more colorful and meaningful prism. You see, I rarely got stuck on a problem—especially in how to start it. Every problem I encountered, I had at least some inkling and general understanding of the approaches required. It doesn't mean I solved every problem correctly. It just means I never got stumped to a meaning-ful degree—*of drawing blank after blank after blank.* Which means I rarely encountered dead ends, unlit paths, or red lights—long, long, red lights—in my math problems. Answers were always nearby. It was generally a smooth, downhill road of flashing green, with no signifi-cant stops. A constant, fun roller-coaster drop with my jubilant hands in the air. However, in an ironic twist, probably choreographed by the cosmos, my success as a student would partially set me up well for failure as a math teacher—an inability to see the full spectrum of the higher purpose of learning mathematics. My lens was the epitome of the absurd. It was both too clear and cloudy at the same time.

Exiled from struggle, my brain was not wired for patience, for irresolution. Regrettably, some of my teaching career would carry this baggage of *success* . . .

THE FIRST KNOCK FROM THE UNIVERSE

As I mentioned in the previous chapter, I didn't start my high school teaching career until 1997, five years after graduating from my teacher education program at U of T. But, in the summer of 1993, a year into my somewhat shocking unemployment, I did manage to get a sessional instructor position at a local community college. How I got the job is the stuff of cheap Hollywood scripts. It was Labor Day weekend, and I was twenty-nine and living with my parents. It looked quite likely for me to get the George Costanza trifecta—thirties, unemployed, and living at home. Nonetheless, that Friday I started to pack my Honda Civic hatchback for my annual Labor Day camping trip. That's when I got the call.

My friend from U of T, Mike Gadsden, who was one of the lucky ones to full-time time employment (he had a PhD, which helped), was on the phone. Seneca College needed a math and physics teacher. Apparently, there had been a sudden illness, and they needed some-one to teach physics and calculus. This wouldn't be the first time an opening for a teaching job was connected to illness. The first high school teaching job I got at Western Tech was because of a suicide. The second job I got at Riverdale Collegiate, after being displaced, was because the teacher had terminal cancer. My teaching career, at least the early part, seemed like it needed an asterisk to convey some unprocessed, subconscious guilt.

While I was naturally excited about the job prospect, I also realized that it was Friday, and this job was going to start on Tuesday. Mike told me to come in for an interview right away, dressed in my camping sandals and shorts. Before long, the job was mine. I went back home to finish packing. In addition to throwing a tent, sleeping bag, lawn chair, and a cooler of burgers and beers into my trunk, I threw in every physics book I could find, since my physics background consisted of taking one university course, almost all of it forgotten. Not the way I imagined christening my teaching career. Like they christen a new ship with a bottle of champagne, I suppose it would have seemed appropriate to throw a bottle of beer against my car door.

During my three years teaching with Mike at Seneca College, I learned the physics that I'd need for my first high school teaching job. I learned to project my voice while teaching in large lecture halls. I learned to write big in a disarming hand. I also met my future wife. I was twenty-nine and she was twenty-three. We started dating after she quit the pharmaceutical technology program she was in (math and physics were prerequisite courses in the program). *Unfortunately*— there is that word again—all this success kept my teaching vector moving toward completion and correctness for the next three years. I was great at my craft. My explanations were crystal clear, perfectly aping the procedures I had mastered when I was in high school. The problem was, if I can be perfectly transparent, I really had no idea what I was doing for some of the physics and calculus. Marching forward with perfect preparedness and minimal hesitation perfectly thwarted that vector being pointed inward. *Pause. Turn in? Hardly.* "Ready, set . . . go" was my mantra for teaching mathematics.

So, did I really understand the wave nature of light? Did I really understand how and why the chain rule worked? It would take several years before I better understood calculus. And only by the tenth year of my teaching career did I even begin to think I could teach it with the depth and beauty that it demanded. By that time, I would assign calculus questions for homework knowing full well that there were some I wouldn't be able to do when students asked about their solutions in class. *That was the point.* To demonstrate some *real-time teacher thinking* about a problem right in front of your class! All that thinking we do at home, in the math office, or anywhere for that matter, is something kids *never see.* If we need to see that failure is a mandatory concept for learning and *teaching* mathematics, then we need to do a better job of showing our unpolished problem solving. I know that my students' curiosity for mathematics only grew when we were faced with collective irresolution. I guess *Chasing Rabbits* was unconsciously hatched then.

WHITE RABBIT TURNS INTO THE BLACK CAT

Reflecting back, almost every satisfying math problem that I have done has had some measurable moments of stoppage. And, to clarify, I don't mean I took a break from the problem. I mean that I was stuck on the problem, unsure as to what to do next. *The tension of unfamiliarity is probably the most familiar thing encountered in learning mathematics.* Sometimes these moments lasted for seconds. Sometimes minutes. Sometimes a few hours. But never beyond that, as that is when I would get up. Now that doesn't mean I solved the problem. It just means I gave up and moved on. Unbeknownst to me, I was exhibiting a critical idea of play—a necessary component of doing mathematics—that we should be *free to leave* anytime we want. Not everything needs to be solved if we want to truly embrace an idea of wellness in mathematics.

In 2019, I was asked to give an Ignite Talk at NCTM's Annual Exposition and Meeting in San Diego. Five minutes. Twenty slides that auto-advance every fifteen seconds. The title of my Ignite was "The Zeroth Lessons." The format demanded a quickness that I *refused* to give. After the title slide, my first two slides were blank. In fact, I used my first fifteen seconds to remain silent, creating a pause that must have felt both awkward and intriguing to the audience of one thousand.

My first words were not intended to pierce the silence, but to pay *homage* to it. I spoke confidently, but quietly and slowly, completely lacking any adherence to the concept of making my message *quick*. All the math problems that flat-out stumped me were dancing in my head, celebrating, knowing that I was going to use this stage, in front of a sea of math educators from all over North America, to honor and give gratitude to the most unheralded gift of mathematics. My fourth slide after a minute of golden silence and no images had a person staring up at a beautifully lit sky of thousands of stars. Written on the slide was "Stillness Is the Language of the Soul."

Stillness and pausing are cherished but rather rare gifts in Western society. Reflecting on all the moments in our lives where such gearing down occurs—listening to music, reading a book, looking at art, staring at flowers, and so on—we must surely agree that these moments, fleeting and generally undocumented, add a quality and richness to our lives. If you have a sweet tooth, you have surely had a dessert where the movement of your fork/spoon through the last few bites has slowed down to something Zen-like. In mathematics it is no different. Correction: *should be no different*. Stillness in math is unheralded in its beauty. You hopefully have experienced it. It goes something like this . . .

A problem that captured your interest and attention. You noodle and doodle through the initial stages with some clarity and confidence. You think you see some light. But it dims out. You chase this vague illumination. It leads you back to where you started. Maybe an hour or so in, you are frustrated. *However*, you are not clenching your teeth or banging your fists against a desk. You are captivated by your entanglement. Only you will have memory of this struggle, which will not only strengthen resolve for the future, but will never be seen bleakly or regrettably. Maybe a slight, self-comforting massaging of your forehead with three or four fingers now begins. Resignation is setting in. You keep staring at the problem, but you have stopped thinking. Your gaze is both focused and blurry, simultaneously.

Unconsciously, you have experienced the highs and lows (both valuable)—far, far more lows—of the thousands of mathematicians who have come before you. Mathematics, in its historic garment of choice—a dark cloak—has cast a spell of stopping your thinking, hopelessly, yet romantically, frozen by the arithmetic or algebra riddle before you. But you at least saw some flickering light. One of the most famous mathematicians in history, Andrew Wiles, summed up this darkness with the poetic uplift as only he could have. His words describe his front row seat to the mathematical theater of the absurd:

> Perhaps I could best describe my experience of doing mathematics in terms of entering a dark mansion. You go into the first room and it's dark, completely dark. You stumble around, bumping into the furniture. Gradually, you learn where each piece of furniture is. And finally, after six months or so, you find the light switch and turn it on. Suddenly, it's all illuminated, and you can see exactly where you were. Then you enter the next dark room . . .

The word *dark* appears in Andrew Wiles's quote four times. I'm quite sure he spoke from his seven years of being locked in the dark castle of Fermat's last theorem, culminating in a proof in 1993, three and a half centuries after it was proposed by Fermat himself. Given the six months Wiles describes taking to find the light switch, fumbling in the dark attests to an allegiance to slowness, to stopping and starting over as many times as needed. That's why it didn't matter that many of the mathematicians in the audience when Wiles unveiled his proof to the world were probably unable to fully understand his mathematical testimony. The point wasn't to understand as much it was to celebrate darkness—and the *illumination* it gives of what is inside of us. Charles Darwin, more well-known then even Andrew Wiles, came to a similar conclusion about mathematics: "A mathematician is a blind man looking in a dark room for a black cat which isn't there."

The black cat often shows up and stays in time intervals well beyond our own lifespans. It's a daunting reality, but there is something to be mined. Peter Harrison and I accidentally went into these caves in the early 2000s.

THE 1,000-HOUR EXAM

I know what you might be saying. That while these stops are beneficial, the realities of the classroom are certainly not set up to incubate such sluggish mathematical reflections. While that is certainly true, students should be given space and time proportional to what is available—or can be made available—to at least honor the truth of what it is to *think and feel like a mathematician*. I mean, what is the point of mathematics if one is not actually engaged in thinking like one? So where is the classroom compromise? While many mathematical ideas came late to me, the notion of giving students mathematical problems that came preinstalled with mathematical safety signs, like "Yield," "Slow Down," and "Stop," did not. And the genesis for all of this transpired over a spring dinner in 2003. Yeah, you guessed it, with Peter Harrison.

Peter and I only taught one course together while we were at Riverdale Collegiate in Toronto: Geometry and Discrete Mathematics. But it was that single experience, specifically what happened in the final months of the course, that became the mathematical muse responsible for the chapter you are now reading—essentially an inspiration for writing this entire book. Facilitating this, and not to be lost here, is that Peter and I were more than colleagues by that point. We had become friends. The banter. The effortless swimming of discussion topics of travel, books, music, food—especially curry—soccer, and mathematics that defined our first dinner would define all our dinners. That the space for our dialogue regarding mathematics was colored and disarmed by other mutual interests must be given credit for what eventually ensued.

While eating dinner one evening, Peter asked, "So, who is writing the final exam?" He didn't ask it in an enthusiastic way. He asked it like he was dutifully checking off an inventory box. I think I responded back with a similar disinterest. In this collective ennui with traditional assessment, we found a disruptive nugget of gold. Keep in mind, this was 2003. The times were not conducive to disruption. The internet was in its infancy. None of the big social media platforms existed yet. The flow of communication and knowledge moved vertically toward institutional expertise and preference. Twenty-first-century math education began with little change from the century before. Emphasis on traditional curriculum and assessment continued without opposition. But Peter Harrison was one of the most respected and well-known math educators in Ontario, so he was given a lot of rope to do things. I simply followed his lead.

The students that Peter and I taught were among the brightest in the school. Almost all of them had proven their mathematical mettle over the previous eight months, and all of them had already been accepted into the universities of their choice. As such, many had unofficially checked out. Even though they were some of the keenest math students in the school, they were still teenagers who wanted to coast through the last few months of high school. So giving them a clichéd exam of the year's greatest hits in a two-hour writing block seemed anticlimactic—and almost an insult to the students, to us, and to mathematics. As if our course were a blockbuster film, we needed a dazzling climax! But what?

Peter suggested that we look at the fifty-five culminating problems in the back of our textbook—of which he was one of the authors. His idea was that we each pick six, hand these twelve questions to the students, and tell them that five would be on the final exam in six weeks. It took me a fraction of a second to figuratively leap out of my seat to accept this wonderfully unconventional idea! Over the weekend, we chose our problems and put them all on a single double-sided piece of paper.

Those fifty-five problems at the back of the book are special. They are not your typical problems. As such, they carry an encouraging warning that failure lies ahead—not sure you will ever see "encouraging warning" in a sentence ever again! It was the first time I ever saw a written introduction to math problems that informed the brightest math students in Ontario (this course was harder than calculus) that they were going to get stuck—a lot. About damn time! It reads:

> The problems in this section offer you the opportunity to solve some significant problems related to the topics you have studied throughout the course. Several problems can be solved in more than one way. Some of the problems are challenging. Considerable ingenuity may be needed to solve them. You may be unable to complete a solution at the first attempt. You may find it helpful to work with others, to share ideas and strategies. Be persistent—try a problem, set it aside, try it again later, or try another strategy. It may take several days, or even longer to solve some of these problems.

Sigh. I wish I had had these words of mathematical warning when I was a high school student. We handed out this "dirty dozen" in class and told the students the format. The reaction was a mix of bewilderment and intrigue. We told them there would be class time to work on the problems together. The "worst case" scenario would be that the weakest student would memorize twelve detailed solutions of geometric proofs and problems. We were more than okay with that.

The days we gave students class time to work on these potential exam questions had some of the best classroom energy I have ever experienced. Students working in groups, in pairs, and in isolation. Students moving around. Students scrawling their ideas on paper and the chalkboard. Students trying their best to run their ideas by us to see if they could break our poker faces. Freeing mathematics freed our students to think deeply, calmly, and passionately about the problems in front of them. This beehive of deep thinking, which was their home for around thirty days, was the epitome of wellness. Mathematics was alive and so were our students.

One of the five problems that appeared on the "final exam" was problem 33:

> P is a point inside a square. The distances of P to three of the four corners are 3, 4, and 5 units respectively. Find all possible lengths of the side of the square.

A square and three consecutive single-digit numbers. Does it get any simpler than this in terms of information and familiarity at the high school level? This is about as low-floor as you can get in terms of *every student wanting a piece of this question.* The problem is, the mathematics required for all the different solutions requires not just an understanding of high school topics but also a fearlessness and thirst for creativity. Don't bother rummaging through all your successful mathematical conquests to find a similar problem. Not only will that search bear little fruit, but it kind of defeats one of the joys of mathematics—to try completely new problems!

My own personal solution to this question was rather laborious, a painstaking ordeal through three hardly pleasant-looking equations in three unknowns. I should have been happy with the solution, but I wasn't. I wanted to find something elegant by being crafty. I just didn't have it on this problem. But one of our students most certainly did. Her solution was the easiest mathematically, only employing elementary high school trigonometry. However, it is also one that I probably never would have found. While doodling on a geometric diagram is something that is second nature to me, my mathematical graffiti is limited to just adding and extending lines—which a couple of the solutions do in fact demand. My own personal toolbox does not contain the brilliant first step of this student, Yanna Kang.

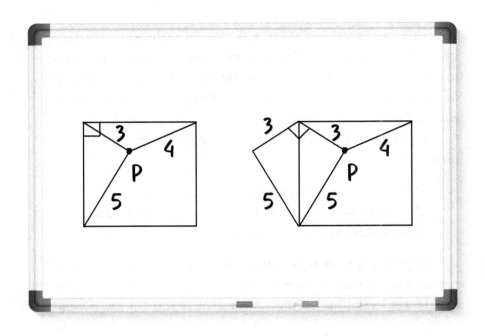

She rotated the top triangle out of the square and recognized the integrity of the 90-degree angle after that ¾ counterclockwise rotation. Toss in some Pythagoras, and the rest was a small buffet of high school trigonometry in those two adjacent triangles. Game over. After Yanna's initial masterstroke, the rest of the solution was anticlimactic. Her initial move was the key to unlock the door. When I asked her how she ever thought of doing that, she humbly and unsatisfyingly remarked, "Not sure." But she also told me her idea didn't come to her for a few days. *A few days.* That is well beyond the expiration date of the two-hour exam—that she thankfully didn't have to take! Even Yanna, one of the brightest students I have ever taught, would not have manufactured *that* solution in *that* time frame. She would probably have gotten close to a perfect paper if we would have chosen to go with a traditional piece of assessment—where too much stopping is seen as a sign of weakness. Only when stopping was seen as both a necessity and a luxury in mathematics, did we get to finally see the colorful and creative mind of Yanna Kang. It was beautiful. It was a great way to finish off the course. Peter retired to teach in Hong Kong that year. It seemed fitting that our professional relationship ended with such mathematical color. For a brief moment in time, I had nothing to rant about.

DRINKING IS THE ONLY SOLUTION

As I mentioned earlier, I rarely encountered and valued stop signs in mathematics when I was a student. I considered long pauses to signal a deficit in my understanding. That is because I was never given math problems that basically said, "Here, you seem smart, go fail this question a dozen or so times . . ." I was deprived of mathematical failure in my youth. I now cherish and long for it in my middle age. One of my favorite problems that initially baffled me appeared in the *Guardian*, courtesy of Alex Bellos, author of several wonderful math books, including my favorite, *The Grapes of Math: How Life Reflects Numbers and Numbers Reflect Life*. The problem involved a bottle that contained 750 cubic centimeters of whiskey.

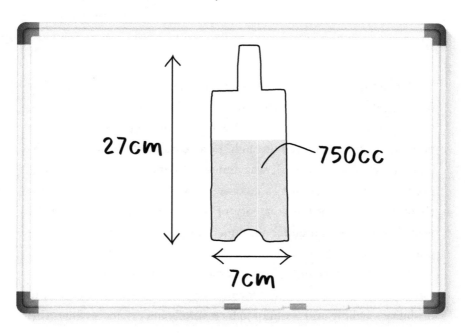

The question looks at the aftermath of drinking some of the whiskey: How much whiskey has been consumed? The nonuniform shape of the bottle meant that proportional reasoning wasn't going to work as a strategy—that itself is a good insight to flesh out with students.

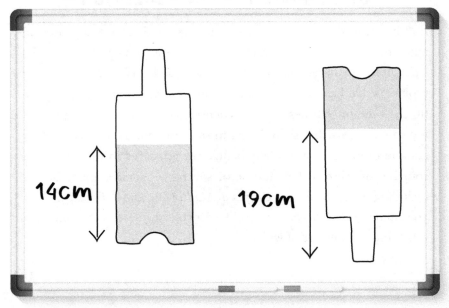

Since this question was offered up by the great Bellos, I knew that the elegant solution lay outside the conventional trappings of algebra. Fifteen years ago, when presented with the square problem from the previous section, I labored through the algebra dutifully and unflinchingly to get to a solution. It was almost all perspiration—no inspiration! But with this problem, subconsciously at least, my brain—maybe channeling some of the creativity of Yanna—refused to yield to the worn-out road of simultaneous equations that lay ahead. With some poetic defiance, I chose to look for the road less traveled.

In mathematics, doing this has meant—as it has meant for thousands and thousands of years for every mathematician of every kind of ability—willing and wanting to be mentally in park for a while. This might explain why I don't mind traffic snarls or long lines at the grocery store. Patience is not your ability to wait; it is your *attitude* while you wait. In mathematics, one's attitude while in limbo not only affects the outcome of the question, but really, the outcome of one's view on mathematics altogether. Being interested in only the answer is like only wanting to know the ending of a great book or film. Mathematics has slow-baked patience into me, and the whiskey problem was a classic case of offering up a whole bunch of nothing and plenty of hemming and hawing. I stared at the numbers 14 and 19 over and over again, until they bored to no end. My mind then just casually drifted to something else, just to break up the monotony. I looked at the numbers not there in the first picture—the height of 13 of the empty part of the bottle with the neck. And almost immediately, my head flipped to see that the empty part of the bottle, when turned upside down, would "fill up" to 19. These two parts of the bottle looked identical, but one had more of the whiskey. What if . . . ?

What if. The potential turning points in life invariably hang on this statement. In mathematics these two words symbolize the energy, play, creativity, and fearlessness required to keep chasing rabbits and black cats. Often, this leads more to failure. But failure in mathematics, as we are discovering, means something completely different than how it is historically interpreted in society. We delve deeper into this in the next chapter. The second half of Erin Hanson's short poem speaks to what awaits if we dive headlong into math failure.

> ## And you ask, "What if I fall?"
> ## Oh but my darling, What if you fly?
> ### —Erin Hanson

In mathematics, "what if" surfs some of the fearlessness of uncertain decisions that we all need to make when posed with a great math problem. It is like having an infinite number of keys at your disposal to open just one or two doors. Sometimes you get lucky, and you can open the solution door by trying only a few different keys. Other times, it might seem you have tried them all, and you will still be locked out of a solution. Don't despair. You are at the heart of mathematics where it beats the loudest. Your passionate persistence is flight itself. Getting the solution lifts you higher. A modern-day example of this would be someone like Julia Robinson, who devoted two full decades trying to solve Hilbert's tenth problem (David Hilbert posed twenty-three problems in 1900 at a conference in Paris that he hoped would be solved by the end of the century.) The problem consumed her life, even though a final solution evaded her for almost a third of it. Her passion and almost unparalleled devotion to mathematics make her a modern-day heroine. A festival that celebrates the joy and transcendence of mathematics is named after her: the Julia Robinson Math Festival.

Naturally, I won't share with you the key that worked in the whiskey problem. That would be selfish. Yes, *selfish*. I don't want to rob you of you figuring it out for yourself! I spent several hours on this problem, and 99 percent of it was in that all-too-famous realm of zero progress. The price for success never comes cheap in great math problems. You have to give a mile to gain an inch. Chasing a solution in some math problems often comes at the paradoxical speed of zero. These are the problems that grip us. These are the problems that suspend the world around us. These are the problems that serenely mine our patience, creativity, and thirst for mathematical diversion. These are the problems that we chase in our lifelong journey of mathematics. Be fiercely in the moment. Look for and cherish your own triangles rotated out of squares. There is no arrival in this journey—for anyone. Mathematics will always remain an unfinished trek, and we should feel satisfied— paradoxically, I suppose—with no final landing spot.

A decade ago, a young Dan Meyer told the world in his TEDx talk "Math Class Needs a Makeover" that students needed "patience for irresolution." He was spot-on for nailing down one of the key attributes needed in problem solving. However, I would say that if this chapter, and the whole book for that matter, is to have any meaning, it is that all of us need *passion* for irresolution. But stopping in our mathematical thinking is not the only place where heavy time-outs need to happen. We need to stop and reevaluate the most macro ideas of how and why we want to educate our children in mathematics. We need to look not only inside our world of math education, but outside of it as well. We need to stop and pause and examine our dormant, inner relationship with math. Wellness is an internal desire and construction. That's good, because so is the essence of mathematics.

QUADRANT II

What you read next was written just days after I found out about the passing of John Berray, whom this book is dedicated to. John Berray was a San Diego math teacher whose radiance radiated—there are very few people who can earn such heavy alliteration—well beyond the limits of this beautiful, coastal city. As such, there is only one person who can and should close this chapter.

John Berray was a person who gave thought and time to anyone and everyone. A person who would come into his classrooms on the weekends and put a final coat of whiteboard paint on all the desks. A person who would create an energy field of love and kindness that assured you he was listening to you, creating lasting bonds of friendship.

In 2018, at California Math Council-South in Palm Springs, where I met John for the second time, he gave a quietly modest Ignite Talk called "Schedule Quadrant II." John only knew quietly modest. While his impact on math education was deafening, John spoke with a softness colored by his humanity and hope for math education. That softness had a unique amplification quality that allowed his words to transmit widely and affectionately. One of his great transmissions of poignancy was his five-minute Ignite. John Berray walked softly, but carried a big heart, instead of a stick. That heart was the center of his words to the thousand people that were in attendance. That we need to take care of us—important things that just don't seem to get prioritized in our often self-perpetuated busy lives. We would find these things in quadrant II.

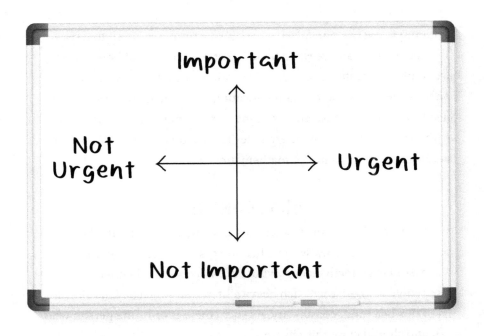

The graph has four quadrants similar to graphs students encounter in middle school. The first quadrant is the upper right. Here, John tells us we would find things like delivering lessons, attending to student needs, and putting out fires. The quadrant below would include something like a spilled soda. John's warmth and sense of humor were omnipresent. It's why he wanted us to live more in quadrant II—important but not urgent. The things that we find in this generally unattended, upper-left quadrant are the gold doubloons of human richness. As John pictorially referenced in his talk, quadrant II provides the real treasure of facilitating this lifelong pursuit of mathematics.

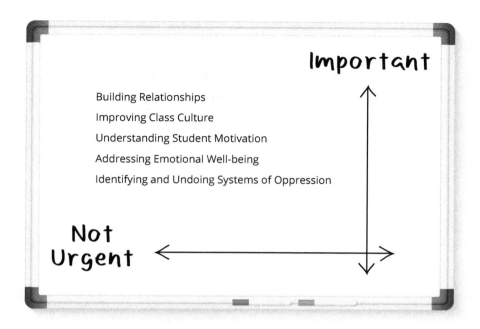

So many kids are suffering with math anxiety, grappling with classroom experiences that darken their lives and put immense pressure on them to perform and achieve success defined in terms of standards and grades. In this decade of rehumanizing mathematics and revolting against the unhealthy conditions that many students learn in, we are being given the gift of one big flashing red light. This is the "stop" that we must pay attention to. If not, we risk further psychological and emotional injury to our students. Bertrand Russell, one the most influential people of the twentieth century in mathematics and education, asked a question that was paraphrased from his book *On Education*: "Do we love our children enough to make them what they can become, free citizens of the universe?" It's been almost a hundred years since Russell made that reflection. It's been almost a hundred years that it's gone unanswered.

Mathematical wellness is about freedom. Edward Frenkel, author of *Love and Math*, said, "Where there is no math, there is no freedom." These days, the same institutions that suffocate mathematics inflict the same damage on our children. Let's take the power of the mathematical pause to reflect on all of this. Let's spend far more time in quadrant II. Let's carry the soft and kind wisdom of John Berray to offer pause to the humanness that drives us. And see how that is the only way to drive math education. Let's pull over. After all, we're not going anywhere.

FUMBLING
TOWARDS ECSTASY

The middle is messy, but it's also where the magic happens.
—Brené Brown

Many of you will recognize the following image, which was crafted by Tetsuya Miyamoto back in 2004.

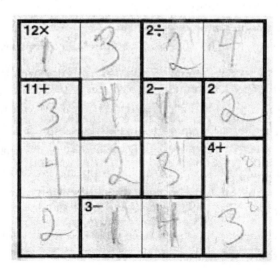

KenKen, the puzzle Miyamoto created, is now available in over two hundred publications, including the *New York Times*, which was the first US paper to run the puzzles back in 2009. The rules are simple: In an n x n grid, use only numbers 1 to n (in this case, 1 to 4). Also, no horizontal or vertical line can use any number more than once. Finally, the numbers in the heavily bolded regions must correspond to the bolded result. For example, the numbers in the L-shaped region in the upper left must multiply to 12. Simple and seductive.

I chose the above image specifically because there is evidence of *erasing*—a sure sign thinking and recalculating were happening. Most of mathematics involves invisible thinking not easily evident in the final product, or at all. The longer the distance of contemplation before commitment to a possible idea with pen or pencil, the healthier will be our understanding and appreciation of mathematics. What pillars of wellness sit in this wide stretch of hemming and hawing about math? The mental one is fairly obvious, with such a strong obligation to creative problem solving. Spending consistent time in this space allows us to better understand ourselves in connection with mathematics. We become comfortable with who we are. Our emotional learning is supported by how we ponder the math in front of us. We allow ourselves to begin to be comfortable with confusion, doubt, and hesitancy, normal reactions in mathematics. We just need more explicit consideration of all of this in math education—education must be broadened to house these ideas. Our intentions must be explicit with mathematical wellness inside the classroom.

Miyamoto himself had a long and trying journey to reach the state of wellness mathematics would ultimately lead him to. When he was fourteen, he was in a low-level school, a place where he felt bored and anxious. He eventually dropped out. But emptiness and loneliness still had a stranglehold on him. He contemplated suicide more than a few times, as his life felt completely small and out of focus. Mathematics would provide the tonic for that emotional disconnectedness, beyond anything Miyamoto could ever have imagined. His story is so captivating that the *New Yorker* did a piece on him in 2020, as well as a twenty-five-minute documentary.

In that article, Miyamoto, who went on to become a teacher, talks about something called "nervous air," something that caused him great angst and despair while he was in that depressing school. However, and this is important, Miyamoto wanted to channel and redirect that nervousness into something positive. His puzzles became the beneficiaries of this sublimating energy. In 2004, KenKen was born. Evidence of how powerful his puzzles were in creating intense focus was demonstrated in his classroom in 2011. That was the year of the Great Sendai Earthquake. As aftershocks rattled on, students in his class, while doing his KenKen puzzles, did not even lift their heads. Potential danger was at hand, but the body language of the students suggested that they were unfazed by the tremors. Doing math in the face of physical danger? Really? In fact, we will find out later that very idea has been mythologized and became a source of inspiration for a very famous mathematician!

An excerpt from the *New Yorker* captures his feelings on his work: "Miyamoto treats each of his puzzles as a life; they are hand molded to tell a story in patterns of math. In 2016, onstage at Google's offices in New York, in an ill-fitting suit, Miyamoto described the purpose of his pedagogy in ancient Greek terms: the point is to secure eudaimonia, or, as he put it, the 'happy life.'"

The pencil and paper simplicity of Miyamoto's puzzles created a bridge between the suicidal despair of a teenager and the philosophical mindfulness of an adult. Though the math is pretty standard arithmetic, when nested in creative puzzle-making, magic occurs. A portal to the loftiest ideas of life opens up—for everyone. The pleasure lies in this messy middle, juggling precise mathematical hints, options, and constraints with infectious charm, drawing you in more and more to Miyamoto's mathematical heart. Simple sleuthing, but it takes fumbling, contemplation, and confusion to get there. And what is the best place to instill thinking about mathematics in this fumble-forward way? Why, in a first grade classroom! That enthusiastic proclamation comes as a result of not years of research, but the collision between fate and foolishness.

AN ODD INTRODUCTION

In 2015, two years after I quit teaching, the Right Angle—my dream of a math store/school made concrete—burned down. The Right Angle could have been this wonderful locus of math games, books, and after-school classes. I lost everything. However, my ideas for what a beautiful mathematical experience should look like for every student did not. And without this devastating loss, I wouldn't have been given the opportunity to see life through an impoverished lens. I wouldn't have been given the gift of failure, and of now navigating my life with the priority of looking inward. Part of my baby steps toward repurposing my life came through my own daughter, Raya.

Just after the fire, Raya, who was in first grade at the time, asked me with the honesty and earnestness of a six-year-old if I would want to visit her math class. She was cutely naive in asking, and I was equally naive in accepting. I mean, what was a high school math teacher going to do with a classroom of students who have probably only mastered counting and some single-digit addition and subtraction? My enthusiastic acceptance of my daughter's invitation should have at least been tempered by the realities of a first grade class and their limitations. *Luckily, I wasn't that smart.* In a few days, forty minutes of number theory, in the form of Unifix cubes, awaited twenty or so inherently curious children. That's right. Number theory.

The day of my visit, I sat in my car in the school parking lot for at least fifteen minutes before getting out. My bags of cubes were in the passenger seat. My presentation was loosely floating around my head. It hadn't been beta tested. Number theory with first graders? They don't even do that in high school! I don't think I was sitting in the car out of nervousness—maybe, instead, I was experiencing subconscious excitement about what would happen next.

I entered the school and checked in at the main office. While I knew the office staff and the administration, nobody knew I was coming except Raya's first grade teacher. I was volunteering, and really, my only claim to fame at this point was being a disgruntled high school teacher. When I came into the classroom, the kids were already sitting close to the front. Raya was blushing with pride. After the introduction, I pulled out some preformed towers of Unifix cubes—all the numbers from 1 to 10. It was important to give a visual to the kids that was in their wheelhouse.

They could see that the cubes were growing by one with all the familiar counting numbers seen in so many elementary classrooms. But what was *he* going to do with them? Well for starters, remove half of them . . .

Whether or not kids knew that the numbers left were odd was immaterial. They must have had a gut feeling about them and their relationship to each other—jumping by two starting from one. Sure enough, when I asked kids to describe what was left, their responses all swirled around the explicit description of the numbers—1, 3, 5, 7, and 9. Some actually knew that these were called odd numbers. I asked them to tell me everything they knew about these odd numbers. One student started listing some more—which was quite impressive! However, beyond knowing that they "jumped by two" and started at 1, there wasn't much more they could offer. Now, for first grade students—and for most students for that matter—this kind of general description is kind of the limit. I asked again if anyone knew anything else about odd numbers, mysteriously squinting to suggest that there was indeed more—plenty more. One hand was up that wasn't supposed to be: Raya's, my daughter.

With only her hand up at this point, my presentation was mildly inflicted with the impression of being canned. I had told her the night before that I wouldn't be calling on her, since she already knew some of what I was going to share. Sigh. I guess I should have been more explicit. So, with her waving hand and beaming eyes, I called on her. She told the class that when you add two odd numbers, you always get an even.

Sure enough, we picked some random single-digit odd numbers, added them (I wrote the responses on the board), and confirmed that this was true. But I wanted the kids to really think like mathematicians. So, I asked, "Always?" Most of them were sure it was always, but because I asked the question, they had some doubt. Maybe it wasn't? Maybe *super-duper*, large, odd numbers have strange properties? Either way, I managed to inject some uncertainty. Doubt is the bedrock of thinking in the scientific world. It also wields some power in mathematics, making our thinking efficient, despite this braking mechanism. The safest way to instill doubt is through age-appropriate narrative. For young students, that needs to be more fantasy than practicality. While mathematics is about universal truths, the path to these truths is invariably littered with false ideas that were audited by doubt. For students to have the idea of doubt early in mathematics sets them up to demand proof—and the earlier, the better.

I asked the kids if they wanted me to prove that all pairs of odd numbers when added will always give you an even number. Their "YES" came in a burst of shouts and almost involuntary raising of hands. The natural curiosity and intrinsic demand to "know" flooded this first grade class. I went to the well of Paul Lockhart, specifically his first book, *A Mathematician's Lament: How School Cheats Us Out of Our Most Fascinating and Imaginative Art Form.* Lockhart used a simple doodle to prove our rule. I used cubes instead and some goofy kid lingo that would surely make them laugh: "Odd numbers always have their butts sticking out . . ."

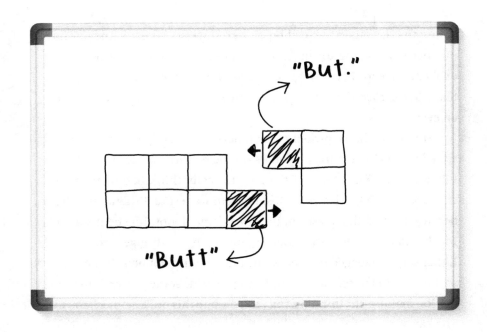

Yup. That got the expected laughter. You would think by the "oohing" and "aahing" that the surprises surrounding odd numbers had peaked. Far from it. I then pretended to dial it back down to something less surprising. I asked them, "What does one plus three equal?" Some shouted "Four!" right away, while others did a careful computation with their fingers. I made sure to positively acknowledge the students who used the finger strategy, informing the kids that you should use your fingers whenever you want or need to. I then asked, "What does one plus three plus five equal?" More kids went to their fingers this time and there was a slightly longer pause. Wonderful! But soon I heard the correct answer: "Nine." I wrote these sums on the board and asked if they could see anything special—really special. Sure enough, the kids looked at the whiteboard with equal concentration and bewilderment. As they stared, I told them they probably couldn't see what I saw. I told them I had *special vision*. Naturally, they became curious about this vision and the whole focus on odd numbers.

As I closed my markers, indicating that no more writing would be done, I offered a cryptic description of odd numbers. I told them that all odd numbers, except for 1, are block-letter "L-shaped." Sure enough, those Unifix cubes, which had sat unattended to for the last little while, were fashioned into the twelfth letter of the alphabet. Math came to life, and so did the entire class. The "oohs" and "aahs" were replaced by gasps and bulging eyes, indicating how mind blowing this all was. I glanced back at the board and started adding these newly configured odd numbers. Sure enough, 1 + 3 was equal to 4, but *this* 4 was a square! I took my square and tucked it into the L-shaped five. What? Another square (3 x 3)! This continued until all the single-digit odd numbers were snuggled in to make a square of 25. The kids were speechless. They were overwhelmed by the simplicity, patterns, and beauty of math. And this was just the warm-up activity!

THE PERFECT LESSON

I held up a "6" built with Unifix cubes. I made sure that everyone counted to six with me. I told them, in an attentive but *shhh-this-is-a-secret* voice that six is a perfect number. I asked who wanted to know why. All twenty-three hands went up in the air.

Now, let's remember. These are six-year-old kids. They don't know—or care for—things like divisors, factors, etc. I needed to come up with something as kid-approved as "butts." I decided on "testers." (For 6, these would be the proper divisors, 1, 2, and 3). These would be the cubes to see if they "went into" other numbers. The mathematics was not being compromised. I was simply using language that would not interfere with their pleasure of seeing why six was a perfect number. I grabbed my testers. I took the 1 cube and counted how many times it went into 6—running it along the length of the 6 cubes. I made sure that the kids counted along with me. One works! I now tried the 2 cube, again sliding/hopping it along the length of 6 cubes. The kids counted out "Three." I tried the 3 cube. The kids counted out "Two." I picked up the 4 cube, and most kids said something like, "It won't fit." There was no mention of division, factors, or multiplying. But that is exactly what kids were in the early stages of processing. I then took the successful testers of 1, 2, and 3 and built them to make a tower of 6—the *same height* as the number we were testing.

Six is a perfect number. The magic of math was now in the room.

I continued testing the numbers 7, 8, 9, 10, 11, and 12.

Seven and 11 were stubborn. Nothing but 1 went into them. For the "perfect number" purpose of this activity, only proper divisors of each number were used. Eight (1, 2, and 4), 9 (1 and 3), and 10 (1, 2, and 5) fell short of being the same height. Twelve (1, 2, 3, 4, and 6) was too tall. Are there any more perfect numbers? If so, what is the next one? These are the questions I asked the kids, rubbing my chin in a cartoonish way.

I put bags of blocks on each table (with groups of three to five students) and asked them to find the next perfect number under

30 . . . "GO!!" The kids began working feverishly to build their towers (they were only building even-numbered towers after a while). They also had to show their successful testers. The whole classroom felt like a game show. Who was going to find this next perfect number? Some false ones were given, but just as quickly as they thought they had the answer, they realized that they had either the wrong testers or had missed a cube. The game continued with unabated electricity—courtesy of both the mathematics and the students.

We were about fifteen minutes into the activity. I could have told them what the next perfect number is and explained why in fifteen seconds. There's no magic there, because there's no messy middle. Without these little kids realizing it, they were going to be skipping through this rich path of thinking for the next thirty minutes. Sure enough, after that time, a group of five girls—who were jumping up and down like they were at a trampoline park—had found that 28 was the next perfect number (1, 2, 4, 7, and 14). They also had their testers to *prove it*.

> # I will say it now, and repeat it ad infinitum: kids don't hate math because it is hard, they hate it because it is boring.

I then asked if they were ready to find the next perfect number after 28. Many seemed up for the challenge. I told them we don't have enough blocks—the next one is 496. Even before they finished their gasping, I wrote 8,128 and 33,550,336 on the board. I turned around to see only bulging eyes. Not that this ice cream needed a cherry, but I threw one on top anyway. I told them that all perfect numbers are *triangle numbers*. Triangular numbers are a sequence of numbers in which each number is represented by dots arranged in the form of an equilateral triangle: 1, 3, 6, 10, 15, 21, 28, 36, 45, and so on.

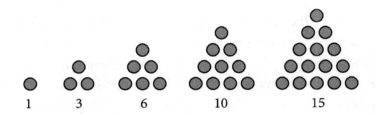

1 3 6 10 15

This opened the door to chase another rabbit through the well-known activity of the "handshake problem."

I asked the students how many handshakes would be required for all of them to greet each other. I told them to stand up, walk around, and start shaking hands. I would keep count. I naturally played the part of a confused scorekeeper, acting out my flabbergasted attempt to keep track of all the handshakes. The socialization was fun, but this strategy was a hot mess. I suggested we start with fewer people. Two. I invited a student to shake my hand. I then invited another student. We all shook hands. Keeping count was easy if the number of people was small. When we got to a group of four, things got interesting, as I reminded students of the *diagonal handshakes*. But, while fun, it was becoming challenging to keep track as I invited more students. It was time to go to diagrams! However, as much as I like drawing polygons and connecting all the vertices, it was rather quickly and unanimously agreed that drawing a twenty-three-sided polygon with "handshake lines" was going to be *too messy*!

People handshakes. Nope. Diagrams. Nope. Time to look for . . . patterns. It is important that the whole sloppy journey of mathematics be shown to students, not just the clean punchlines. Stages 4 and 5 in the illustration below represent the bridge between arithmetic and algebra—we will spend much time trying to find this bridge in chapter five. Students have to naturally exhaust strategies. They have to fail in a healthy space, or else that failure gets married to anxiety and low self-esteem. Honoring failure this way is not compromising mathematics. Honoring failure this way is honoring mathematics—its entire history. Even the patterns of first and second differences here would be impractical if the question asked the number of handshakes for one hundred, one thousand, or a gajillion people (trying to keep to the first grade vernacular here). What better place to instill future curiosity for algebra! That's exactly what I did with my daughter's class. We got to the precipice of algebra in fifteen minutes—and we arrived there *fumbling and laughing.*

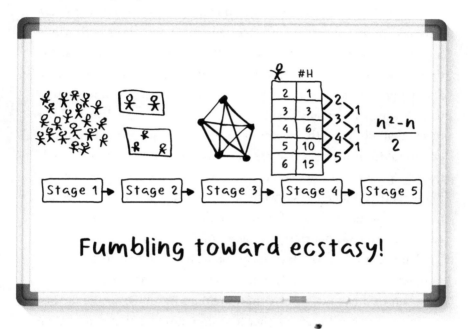

BUOYANT WITH BEWILDERMENT

The scene I just described of a classroom full of first graders enthusiastically journeying into the unknown should demonstrate a key aspect of mathematical wellness: joy. When, as teachers, we model meeting confusion with cheerfulness and exhilaration, our students are sure to follow.

As with so many others around the world, our local schools were beginning to close indefinitely around March of 2020. While our provincial government offered online learning, I wasn't terribly interested in my kids using screen time and technology to do what were basically worksheets. So, I went to one of my go-to resources:

numberphile.com. While I have seen most of the videos, there are always a few that have escaped my viewing pleasure. That pleasure is enhanced considerably if it is something that I can show my kids—and that they would be interested in! And this is how I came across a video about Mertens conjecture.

The bulk of this conjecture is quite accessible, even to middle school kids, like my own. Since Mertens conjecture deals with prime numbers, I thought I would watch this video with Raya, who, at the time of writing this book, now knows her prime numbers up to 223. *She is pushing me to know more.* I was perfectly happy knowing up to 127, which sits snugly beside the binary number 128. I wanted her to see that all the math she knows at this point (except square roots) can spiral into surprises that are pure madness! That even her simple knowledge about primes could take her into some heady ideas about mathematics. But before showing her the video, I slowly unpacked the ideas so it would be easier for her to follow along and get to the very surprising conclusion. Here is what we did.

I made a chart for Raya to fill out. First, she had to list all the numbers 1 to 30 and identify which ones were prime. Easy-peasy. She then had to break down the composite ones into their prime factors. Again, easy-peasy. I then told her to assign numbers that had an even number of prime factors a "+1"; those with an odd number of factors a "−1"; and those which had any duplication (i.e., 20 = 2 x 2 x 5) a "0." The first row in the chart is simply the numbers 1 through 10, which could be stretched out to 100; 1,000; 1,000,000; etc. The second row is the assignment of our numbers, −1, 0, and + 1, based on the above guidelines. The third row is a running sum of these numbers. And, in the beginning, it isn't too exciting, is it?

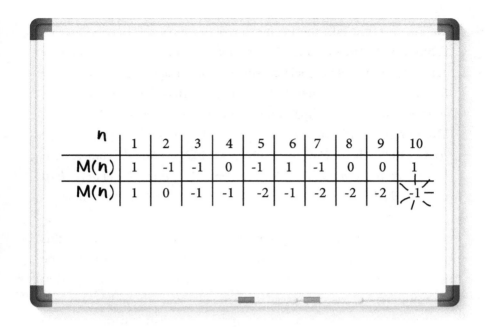

n	1	2	3	4	5	6	7	8	9	10
M(n)	1	-1	-1	0	-1	1	-1	0	0	1
M(n)	1	0	-1	-1	-2	-1	-2	-2	-2	-1

She soon asked, "Why?" I just as quickly said, "Not telling you yet ..." But we can easily find out if we are generating more −1s or +1s by simply adding our integers and keeping a running total. Our gut instinct might say that the total will bob around zero. It seems that the running total is always less than the number n that you are on, right? But it turns out it needs to be even lower than that.

Mertens conjecture involves the square root of these numbers— and being below that! Since Raya knew about squares/square roots, I also asked her to find the square roots of each number from 1 to 30. As she punched in values for nonperfect squares, I told her that she could do this without a calculator and that this method had been known for over three thousand years (since the Babylonians). I wasn't expecting her to take the mathematical bait, but she immediately said, "Show me!" I did, but I told her we would still need the calculator for the repeated division. (Sorry. My history lesson wasn't going to involve long division.)

So, Mertens conjecture is that the running total of +1, 0, and -1 will always be less than the square root of the number you are currently on. For example, take the square root of 9, which is ±3. The −2 in that column sits between 3 and -3. The square root of 100 is 10. When we get to 1,000 and its associated square root of approximately 32, the integer total sits at a paltry 2. Ramping up to 10,000, with a tidy square root of 100, the total dips to a somewhat surprising −23. No matter. This number is still comfortably below 100. At 1,000,000, with a square root of 1,000, the total of these integers is 212. *And so, the conjecture is that the constant summing of the numbers +1, 0, and −1 will never bust out past the boundary of the square root of the number at that point.*

So, does this conjecture hold up? (*Cue suspenseful pause!*) The answer is . . . no! At some point *waaaaaaaaaaay* down the road, this patient summing of the simplest numbers finally breaks through the fortress of the square root. However, we don't know exactly what that number is—we just know it eventually will! All we know is that it probably occurs around something like 10^{400}. The universe isn't big enough to show the scaled graph of this surprising mathematical event!

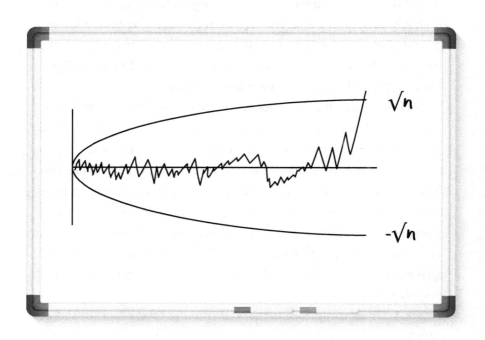

Now, the main reason I wanted to talk about something as obscure as Mertens conjecture is not just the relatively low-floor entry into this problem and its subsequent plot twist; it's the general demeanor of Dr. Holly Krieger, the affable host of this Numberphile video, when she walks viewers through the literal ups and downs of the problem. Her infectious verve climaxes in this kind of communal awe and bewilderment. That her most boisterous emotion is saved for yielding to failure and the unknown. That is the moment, lasting mere seconds, which needs to be bottled—the timeless sweetness of being smitten by the mathematical dance of order and disorder. Sure, I want my daughter to remember the math. But more than that, I want her to remember the natural facial expressions of finding delight in the smallest crevices of mathematics. That a broad and beaming smile from us sometimes occurs in mathematics because it is disorderly and disillusioning. Even when it *lets us down*, we only grow more intrigued and attached to it.

FAILURE LAB

In 2019, I did a campfire presentation at SXSW EDU called "Disrupting Math Education with Punk Ideology." While the title might sound provocative, it's not. The punk ethos involves altruism, the common good, and an intense obligation to one's moral compass—all things that could benefit math education. At the heart of this ideology is a DIY spirit, which will involve buckets of messy middles, and being in the moment with the trials and errors that will be folded into those unvarnished, but wholly shimmering, truths. In this presentation, I played a short but powerful video fusing punk images with mathematical ideas and philosophy. It was a spicy soup! The rest of the hour was taken up by discussion with participants seated in a circle, hence the format name. One of the attendees, Patrick Duffy, whose culturally responsive work in math education I'll share later in the book, made a point that maybe mathematics needs to undergo a rebranding, perhaps change the name to something like . . . Failure Lab. Boom! There it is.

Truthful, disarming, and contemporary. Imagine that class. Kids come in and ask, "What are we doing today?" You, as the teacher of this class, give your best chuckle and respond, "Failing. Lots of it today!"

Let me be clear and direct here before I continue: Our students will only embrace failure if the mathematics captivates them. If not, this failure philosophy goes into the garbage—along with the pedestrian mathematics that gets served up to students every day. Asking students to show perseverance with a worksheet on multiplying decimals or dividing fractions is sending so many wrong messages, I wouldn't even know where to begin. I might even sign up for doing pushups in the rain with a drill sergeant yelling in my ear before doing either one of those torturous activities. Failure needs to be connected to passion— not compliance. Kids are hardwired to accept failure as a prerequisite for success. Case in point: Fay DeFazio Ebert, the youngest person on Canada's national skateboard team.

Skateboarders in general are cut from the punk cloth of *reckless* commitment—to the messy middle of trial and error, experimentation, and failure. When they fall, they are aware that physical damage can be anywhere from light bruising to broken bones. They are also mentally prepared to fail in front of the public. In 2020, when Fay was ten—and a year before she made the Canadian team—an Instagram video of her repeatedly failing on a skateboarding trick went viral. How viral? It was covered by a newspaper based in India. In the video, Fay is attempting to jump over a stack of skateboards at the edge of the skate bowl. She fails five times in a row, each one ending in a different interaction with the hard ground. On the sixth try, she clears it.

What Fay demonstrated is no different than what the students who took the "1,000-hour exam" experienced. Failure and challenge can be linked together as long as there is not only affection for the end result, but also for being in the moment with failure as it happens. There is an ineffable intimacy that grows when we experience these rarefied moments. This has been my mathematical life in a nutshell. My journey with mathematics has catalogued all these moments. My imperfections have been reflected and honored there. We need to show all the arrows of *attempts* so we can humbly and honestly express where we stand with mathematics. The richer the mathematical content, the richer our relationship with our inevitable struggles will be.

One of the best problems I have seen that uses failure as the portal to some pretty cool rabbit holes appeared in the *Guardian*, again by the great Alex Bellos. The problem was titled Getting Coins out of the Bank and it came with a simple setup and one simple rule: There are three coins in the upper-left corner of a grid (think of this array as a two-by-two cell). You have to free all the coins from that area. You have infinite space below and to your right. The only move/rule is that if a coin has a space both directly below and directly to the right, you can remove the coin—but you must replace it with a coin in both of those previously empty positions. The original setup and a possible move are shown below. Can you get all the coins out?

In the picture, a black counter is removed. The replacement for that must be two coins, one below and one to the right.

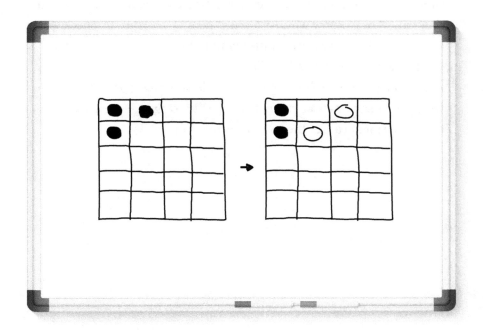

I got large grid paper and used actual coins—hooray for touching and playing with mathematics! I tried various strategies, but after a while, it seemed everything I tried resulted in some gridlock. I kept at it. However, I was seeing this problem only through the lens of a solution. It never dawned on me I should have opened my *unsolvable eye*. Why was I trying to solve this with only my solution eye? I needed repeated failure to begin to instill doubt that an actual solution existed. While the solution of "no solution" was interesting, what was more interesting was the mathematics that supported this futility of trying to get all the coins out. It is one thing for your gut to think there is no solution; it is quite another to be presented with the mathematical argument that there isn't one. And, as in the solution shown by Alex Bellos, some solutions can be elegant while harnessing one of the most despised topics in math—fractions.

My gut instinct said this problem was impossible, even though I had infinite space to jostle around the coins. Why was it impossible to get three coins out with these parameters? That is the question you should ask yourself—and your students. Because if you do, chances are they will want to know why. And warn them in a tongue-in-cheek way that they will need to learn a little about infinity . . .

In the solution posted in the *Guardian*, the grid is marked up as in the image on the following page. While you might be unsure as to why, your mathematical instincts may be kicking in, especially when the replacement rule of the coins is factored in.

For a second, imagine just one coin in the top left-hand corner. Let's give it a value of 1. If we remove it and replace it with one below and one to the right, those coins now occupy the squares that have a value of ½. What happened? Well, literally speaking, *nothing*! The total of 1 is still maintained with ½ + ½. In mathematics, we call this property an *invariant*, that while other things might change—like moving coins around—this thing doesn't. In this case, the total value of the coins must be maintained. Okay, let's expand the idea back to our original question. That means the total value of the coins in our problem is 1 + ½ + ½ = 2. Now let's add the empty square, which is ¼, to get a total of our bank.

Now let's get the sum of the entire area. Which means we can confront students with some cool ideas about *this kind* of infinity: limits, geometric series, and convergence.

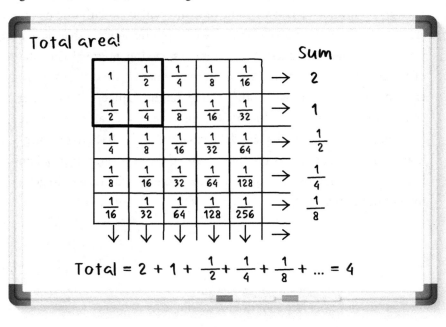

With perhaps the help of a number line, even elementary students can see that the total sum is getting closer and closer to 4. The total area outside the bank, then, simply involves a rather mundane subtraction: the entire area of 4 minus the bank area of 9/4. This leaves us with only 7/4. So that means the area outside the bank, which extends infinitely, can only take on that much value. The problem is, we started with three coins, which, because of their position in the bank, had a value of 2. As such, we don't have enough space outside the bank to allow for this value to exist in any configuration! See, fractions can be fun—*sometimes*.

Let's look backward at this problem for a minute. See how it ends? A comparison of two rather innocuous-looking numbers in terms of their size. The actual final math is not that interesting. What is captivating is how we got there, right? Three scrunched-up coins in an infinite sea of empty squares. A problem that was going to be fumbled around quite a bit, ending in failure every single time. And yet, with these repetitive dead ends, there is an opening for students to get a glimpse of the power of logic, proof, and creative insight. To celebrate and care about the finale, even when a solution is impossible.

All the math we do and think about, whether it can be documented with a flow that is symphonic and seen by everyone or relegated to the "trial and error" sections of our brains and seen by no one, has meaningful value. The value is more about the summation of these mathematical moments. Each one coloring our lives, even if it is merely a dab or a droplet. This is how I am communicating the enrichment of mathematics in our lives to all of you. This is how we all need to communicate it to our students. The ecstasy is for the taking by all of us.

But there is no road to it. *It is the road.* Filled with equal parts clarity and confusion. The KenKen (*ken* meaning "wisdom" or "cleverness") puzzles that Miyamoto created are the yin-yang balance of those two complementary ideas. Clarity and confusion only have alchemical powers when they are combined.

And, the more time you spend on this road, the more you will begin to appreciate that it will not matter whether the road is well paved or rocky, whether you glide or when you stumble. All that will matter is that you are on this road. And so is everyone else. How will *you* be connected with the mathematics? Correct answers with speed? Those who finished their tasks? Correctness and completion have marginalized too many of our students. The heart of mathematics is the fumbling around in the yolk of a mathematical idea or problem. It is easier to show up here in this relaxing forest than the competitive streets of mathematics.

> ## Show up. Be seen. Answer the call.
> ### —Brené Brown

Our connections with each other and the emotions that we share will define the success of this journey. Our emotions are the bonding cement of mathematics. They not only aid in lasting learning of the subject, but more importantly, create a space within us to fondly remember all our intersectional and tangential moments with it. Housed in these memories is the pillar of social wellness.

In the hit television series *Lost*, there were many complex and convoluted storylines, some shrouded with numerical mystery and experiments in physics. Yet, in the final scene of the final episode of the final season, the most important thing was the time that each of the characters spent together and the memories that they made. Mathematics should produce the same lasting distillate of human connection. There is, however, a yawning chasm that needs to be crossed to get us from the twentieth-century mindset of performance to the twenty-first-century mindset of wellness. This chasm can only be crossed together.

HUMANIZATION
IN THE ABYSS

Historically, pandemics have forced humans to break with the past and imagine their world anew. This one is no different. It is a portal, a gateway between one world and the next.
—Arundhati Roy

One of the major lessons of the COVID-19 pandemic, when it came to mathematics, was that the hardened arteries of twentieth-century math education could no longer serve twenty-first-century moral imperatives. What did we generally do? We *dragged carcasses of dead mathematical ideas*, didn't we? Worksheets, graded assignments/tests, answers without understanding, etc., all pushed through the resistance of fiber optic cables—all in the name of the toxic myth that students might *fall behind*. To be fair, we shouldn't blame the medium, as many of us have been learning remotely since the onset of social media channels in the mid-2000s. What we should blame is the anemic content, which was on life support even before the global pandemic. Without emphasis on relationships and our students' mental health, it was rendered obsolete almost immediately.

Career paths and anachronistic practicality can no longer be the main focus, relegated instead to more supporting roles. The toxic performance culture of mathematics will be some of the luggage we will gleefully leave behind. As we tread lightly and softly across the bridge, the abyss will reveal how deeply kindness, wellness, and hope are tied to mathematics, exposing the ways that math is rooted in our intrinsic humanity.

We need to search out the spaces of emotional subjectivity that throw color on the objectivity of mathematics. Mathematics is gifted to us. We hope it is gifted to our students. You cannot, however, treat mathematics as a gift without drenching it in moments of personal reflection and affection. It needs unbounded and unvarnished subjectivity of all the emotions we might have toward it—everything from anger and fear to doubt and confusion to elation and joy. We need to be, as educators, inclusive to all the responses that might come from students. It is the only way for their stories with mathematics to be authentic. And hopefully, over time, their stories move to more positive and healthy ideas of math.

Yet, we withdraw anything resembling this when we talk about mathematics. We need poignant examples where rich mathematics intersects with rich emotions. With much bittersweetness I found one of the richest examples of these on April 11, 2020: the day John Horton Conway passed away from COVID-19.

There isn't too much left to be said about one of the greatest mathematicians and minds of our time. In *Genius at Play*, Siobhan Roberts's biography of Conway, she characterizes the enormity of his personality:

> Archimedes, Mick Jagger, Salvador Dali, and Richard Feynman all rolled into one—a singular mathematician, with a rock star's charisma, a sly sense of humor, a polymath's promiscuous curiosity, and a burning desire to explain everything about the world to everyone in it.

On the day of his death, I watched many videos of Conway. All of them paid reassuring homage to the celebrity stew that Roberts so eloquently described. I then stumbled upon one that put a lump in my throat. It lasted for fifteen seconds, around halfway through a ninety-minute lecture. I didn't see it coming. Nobody could have. I had never witnessed anything so vulnerable, so beautiful, and so emblematic of the humanness of mathematics.

In order to emphasize the impact of what happened at the lecture's forty-minute mark, it's best that I start at the beginning. The lecture was one Conway gave at the University of Toronto in 2017, on the topic of surreal numbers, which he had discovered by attempting to learn the ancient Chinese game Go (the actual name of "surreal" was given by the mathematician Donald Knuth). He opened his lecture with this alluring statement: "I am going to tell you the greatest surprise of my mathematical life."

How is that for creating instantaneous intrigue! Conway shared that while learning Go—which goes back 2,500 years and is played by nearly fifty million people today—he discovered, in his own words, "more numbers than anyone else previously." (He was quick to point out that he did not invent these numbers, only discovered them, highlighting his Platonist belief about mathematics. He was also quick to point out that he never actually got good at Go.) Once again, a tale of accidentally stumbling into rabbit holes pops up.

Even with Conway's charming homespun explanation, my brain felt like a tsunami of information was going through it. It was well beyond my comprehension. Transfinite numbers. Numbers that are greater than all finite numbers, but *not absolutely infinite*. Conway started throwing around the Greek letter omega (infinity) like apple seeds. Cardinal (i.e., five candies) and ordinal (fifth person in line) numbers and their own unique infinities got rolled in. And, at this point, my brain needed to be *rolled out*. But I hung on. Conway always told a good story. Around the forty-minute mark, he told a cracker (keeping it British) of a mathematical tale.

Discussing infinity at great lengths necessitated the mention of Georg Cantor—one of Conway's heroes. After making the mathematical connections between Cantor and the work at hand, Conway drifted into an aspect of Cantor's history that even I, a Cantor fan, was unaware of: he had been instrumental in forming the International Mathematical Union, and he had helped to organize the first International Congress of Mathematicians in Zurich in 1897. Though an interesting footnote in math history, it was hard to tell where this digression was going.

And then, subtle hints in Conway's facial expression revealed that there was to be a more personal dimension to this story. Apparently, there was some uncertainty that the French delegation, led by Henri Poincaré, would show up. For reasons unknown, this would have been a huge personal disappointment to Conway. And just seconds later, Conway confirmed to the audience that there indeed would be a happy ending to this story with a moving shift in his facial expression—he was tearing up. The French did show up, much to the delight of the other fifteen countries in attendance, and to the storyteller Conway, who clapped his hands in a manner suggesting that he would have given anything to be there. What elicited this spontaneous, emotional response to a story that had its drama rooted in something as trivial as who attended a math conference over a century ago? Why did it leave such a heavy imprint? Just a minute or so later, we got a hint, as Conway carried on about going to Halle, Germany, where Cantor died. The essence, the golden nectar of mathematics, has always been its stories. Conway, like many others, was a torchbearer for this. Humanity is not a footnote in mathematics. It's the entire story of mathematics.

He then started talking about his visit to Berlin in the late '80s, prior to the Wall coming down. Realizing he had drifted quite far from his mathematical talk on surreal numbers, Conway remarked to the audience: "I find these stories to be more interesting than the mathematics itself."

And there you go. The emotion—the essential humanity—of mathematics, lies in its stories. Stories that get cobbled together with charming memories. These stories will be our most valuable currency as we reshape mathematics education for the twenty-first century and beyond.

TAKING A LEAF FROM LYDIA

Herodotus, who is widely known as the "Father of History," tells of a critical time in ancient Greece, in the region of Lydia. There was a severe famine, and, as you would expect, plenty of fighting and suffering. It was an extreme situation, which I suppose called for a radical solution. Part of the solution was that the population would only eat *every other* day. What do you think they did on the days they did not? Well, this is one story—there are many others from other countries and civilizations—of how games, much like the ones we play with family and friends, originated. The king of Lydia, Atys, asked that his people distract themselves with games. So, sheep knuckles fashioned for dice games was how the people of Lydia would cope on noneating days. Soon, people became transfixed by these diversions, completely immersed in the playfulness of the simple, communal act of rolling animal bones. A certain level of collective bliss must have occurred because this is how they dealt with the famine for *eighteen years*.

If collective dice games can help people overcome famine for nearly two decades, then surely mathematics must be able to capture our students' curiosity and distract them from their everyday challenges. And no, giving kids worksheets of dividing fractions or factoring questions is not going to cut the mustard here. We need the creative resourcefulness of King Atys. And we need to remind ourselves of mathematics' history of collective endeavor, rather than the largely solo—and *inhumane*—journey through the mathematical wilderness that most students today are made to take. The pressures of this emotionally taxing trip is part of what contributes to math anxiety. Rather than dealing with that anxiety once it has already cropped up, we should be working against it at a much earlier checkpoint.

ALIENATION

As I mentioned in the previous chapter, most children check out of mathematics because it is boring, not because it is hard—but there are some authentically difficult aspects of math that are breeding grounds for math anxiety. I'm talking fractions. They're likely going to be the first gatekeeper in mathematics, as far as both difficulty *and* boredom. Beyond the everyday practicality of knowing some common fractions and their percentage and decimals equivalents, fractions are best understood as supporting actors. They play their best roles in problems about shaded geometric areas where they appear as the awaiting answer at the end, and where working with them correctly is an investigative necessity. Have a go at this one from a kindred math spirit, Ed Southall. It went viral on Twitter in 2018, stumping many because of its ostensibly scant information. Even though getting the answer is tricky, there is no need to have any accompanying text of *What is the area of the shaded region?*

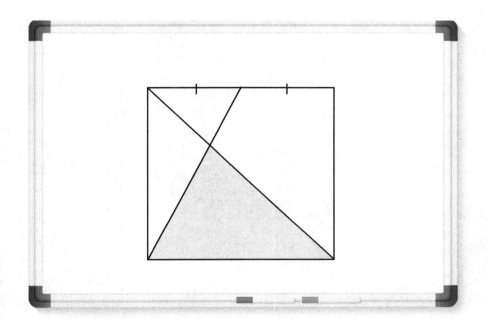

While this is a nice problem with its visual simplicity and could occupy some students for a little while with its perplexity, students in elementary school would not have the required knowledge to work out an answer. Remember, we want to pose problems that invite as many students as possible and to captivate them with a story, some mystery, and perhaps, even a little "weirdness."

Are you familiar with Albrecht Dürer's engraving *Melencolia I*? If you've read Paul Lockhart's *A Mathematician's Lament: How School Cheats Us Out of Our Most Fascinating and Imaginative Art Form*, it may already be etched in your memory. Lockhart's long subtitle pays homage to the magical mathematics quietly embedded in Dürer's engraving.

That's right: the square of numbers in the upper-right corner is a 4 x 4 magic square. It was created in the year 1514, the same year the engraving was completed. As you might be aware, the rows, columns, and diagonals in a magic square will always add up to a constant number—in the case of the Dürer example, it is 34. Looking at this magic square with just the traditional examinations of rows, columns, and diagonals would be a good investigation on its own for students. However, things get even more interesting when we discover that there are a staggering *eighty-six* different ways to obtain this sum! We get these arrangements in rules based on a geometric layout of how these numbers, from 1 to 16, might be connected. Having students just putter around with these numbers, constantly practicing their adding skills while keenly trying to unlock another arrangement, is exactly the kind of regular diet of universal diversion rooted in engagement that we need to feed our math students.

But it is more than that. Students are intersecting mathematics with history and art—Coxeter and Conway would approve of such beautiful overlap.

Now, before you even go any further, you may want to introduce your students to the historic origins of magic squares, and the legendary tale of a young girl, a magic turtle, and an emperor. The whole story is captured in a wonderful book by Dr. Sue Looney, *Ying and the Magic Turtle*, which essentially introduces students to a 3 x 3 magic square: "Long ago in the land of China, there were many rain storms . . . and the land of China was slowly sinking into the sea. This is the story of how a wise emperor, an observant girl, and a magic turtle saved the villages of China from the great flood."

The magic turtle, much like Dürer's engraving, arrives with mystery and mystique. However, the turtle's back can easily be converted to a 3 x 3 square with its nine sections, with the numbers represented by the standard Hindu-Arabic ones. But the turtle would lose its magic—and so would the story. Seeing numbers represented this way draws you in. It feels like there is some universal code to be cracked. Our curiosities are piqued by the strangeness. We are intrigued by this turtle—which metaphorically is really a *rabbit*.

PETER RABBIT I

There is an academic root to the most compelling idea of math alienation: Peter Taylor. Taylor is a professor at Queen's University and the 2006 winner of the Adrien Pouliot Award for outstanding contribution to Canadian math education. He is also the founder of the website rabbitmath.ca—yeah, no coincidences there! Taylor is also Peter Harrison's mentor. Wisdom does indeed flow downhill. I am grateful to know both as mavericks in their fields and as friends.

Taylor offers us this simple statement and following question to think about: "Mathematics is filled with awe and wonder. Why don't we teach it that way?" You know some days we need some bar-talk expletives to color our demands. I can think of a word or two that should come before "teach" . . .

While we mull over that nugget of wisdom (and the imagined colorful language suggested by the author), what have been the repercussions of *not* teaching it that way? Well, Taylor has a sobering answer for that: alienation. Taylor was the first person I know of who identified that the effects of math boredom calcified into alienation. It is at this point those students stop paying full attention to mathematics. Details are missed. Learning becomes more challenging. And, increasingly, teachers are observing the consequence of that alienation: anxiety. Our energies are fixated on dealing with math anxiety when they should be dealing with math alienation.

I think it is important to highlight the philosophy of Taylor's rabbit math. There is an unapologetic poetic affiliation with the concept of beauty. This is from his website: "We are attracted to sweetness and for the same reason we are attracted to beauty—in the first case we needed it to survive, in the second case we need it to thrive. In this remarkable universe of ours, the order and chaos of beauty is a reliable guide to truth."

Though there was no need to include the qualifier "poetic" above, Taylor, in addition to his expertise in connecting mathematics to biology and statistics, also has experience in connecting it to poetry. Namely through his course Poetry and Mathematics, which he has taught for over a decade. Through that language lens, the philosophy of rabbit math drips with the highest purposes of learning. Below is a quote from the website:

> We owe the structure of our curriculum to the pioneering work of Alfred North Whitehead (1920s), who warned that if we failed to pay attention to the stage of Romance, our students' learning would come to naught. And to the insights of John Dewey (1930s), who emphasized the significance of the students' "experience" in their learning. And finally, to Seymour Papert (1970s), who wanted

his students to be sculptors, working together to perfect their creations.

We have failed to pay attention to this Romantic window, where learning has an intrinsic love and creativity that is insatiable. We should rightfully assume that this window occurs in elementary school. Regrettably, we have failed to pay attention to it for a hundred years, since Whitehead issued that warning. Alienation has been the byproduct of this negligence. The following is excerpted from an interview with Peter Taylor where he is speaking about his realization that English textbooks, with their emphasis on stories and art, should be the model for math textbooks (the interview can be found on his university website):

> A crucial difference between English and math curricula is that in English the books come first and the curriculum is then based on these, whereas in math, the curriculum comes first and then the books are based on that. In the first case, the books are essentially artistic; in the second case, the art is lost. . . .
>
> The students never have a chance to be captured by mathematics—in their universe, they give it little credit. And so I think that's where the alienation starts—way back before things are perceived as being difficult in any sense, they are first perceived as irrelevant, essentially meaningless to the student's life. The students say "this isn't me," and shift their attention elsewhere. And then things are missed. And then finally, later, the anxiety comes.

The opposite of alienation is belonging. We need to create spaces in our classroom that honor the identity of each student and allow them the best opportunity to cultivate a Romantic relationship with learning mathematics. We need to create moments of awe and wonder, and fuse those with the relationships we must develop with them as they journey in math. We as educators created math anxiety—not mathematics itself. As such, we should take responsibility for fixing the problem.

BELONGING

It was a late July evening in 2019 when I was out on San Antonio's River Walk with a bunch of kindred spirits who are math revolutionaries by day, and equally spirited revelers by night. In the mix were my Canadian math friends, Kyle Pearce and Jon Orr. There was karaoke going on (which I am proud to say I did not participate in, and *have never* participated in—and never will participate in. Love watching it, but it feels a bit too *lampshadey* for me). That afternoon, I had had lunch with them, along with Kyle's family, who had accompanied him to this Texas math conference. Our friendships in the math communities are heavily aligned to the pedagogy/philosophy of our peers. The stronger the mathematical bond, the stronger the friendship. And when it comes to drilling down to the most micro ideas of our classrooms to find powerful anchors of connection and belonging, few do it better than Pearce and Orr.

A day earlier, I had gone to their workshop, which was unsurprisingly full. I donated a few copies of *Math Recess* to their raffle and planned to sign them after. Kyle and Jon have great synchronicity in their workshops, each offering a unique voice but creating seamless transitions that make the presentation feel whole and connected. Jon went up first. He opened with what seemed like a totally random question: "What do you think is the most popular hotel in Los Angeles?" Not only did I not know the answer, I had zero idea how this could be related to the workshop that lay in front of us. I was stumped, but heavily invested in knowing the answer. I might have been drawing blanks, but I had a gut feeling that the answer would surprise and delight me. I was not disappointed. The most popular hotel in terms of ratings and reviews is the three-star Magic Castle Hotel. There is only one word that should come after that: *Why?* As Jon Orr revealed the answer, he shared images from the hotel, including one of a scene from an ostensibly unremarkable hotel pool, with a red phone that hung on a wall between lounge chairs and above that, a sign that read: "POPSICLE HOTLINE."

Even before he went into more detail, many of us were already connecting the dots. That our time with our students is not measured by minutes, hours, and years, but by moments—*mathematical moments* that resonate with the same whimsy, memory, and connection as dialing up for a Popsicle on a dedicated poolside hotline. Humanity is connected by a red phone with an icy treat on the other end. When we remember fondly, we are piercing the armor of curriculum, expectations, and mastery. We are creating the fertile ground for being wooed by the magic of mathematics.

In Richard Linklater's Oscar-nominated *Boyhood*—which he filmed over the course of twelve years—the final scene shows the central character, Mason, now a college student, sitting on a hill beside a girl he has just met, Nicole, watching the sunset in Big Bend Ranch State Park in Texas. They are both smitten with the physical and emotional colors of the moment. One last deep philosophical reflection remains. Nicole turns to Mason and says: "You know how everyone is saying seize the moment? I don't know, I'm kind of thinking it's the other way around. You know, like the moment seizes us."

Kyle and Jon are giving their students mathematical moments all the time, moments that are there to be seized. Mathematics rises above the mundane and gets filed away in our memories. Quilting together many of these moments is the essence of learning mathematics—as we find our way back to starting again. Starting again is to rehumanize mathematics. Rehumanizing mathematics means building connections and relationships. So that when we focus on the moments—that seize us—there is a natural place to share and celebrate them.

RESET IN THE ABYSS

The desire to reset math education as we know it has been gaining momentum in recent years—though the pace car of education has never really fired on all cylinders. Any ideas of what a new frontier of math education could look like have been at the mercy of a Model T mindset rather than a state-of-the-art Tesla. What's slowing things down are entrenched Western ideas about math education that emphasize career, application, and practicality over a sense of humanity, and yes—over wellness.

Having a rich spiritual life is a key facet of humanity for many of us—and remember, the spiritual is also an essential pillar of wellness. Affirmation of the spiritual aspects of mathematics can come from the most unlikely of places. For example, when the actor David Krumholtz signed on to play mathematician Charlie Eppes on *Numb3rs*, he hadn't had a previously positive relationship with math. In fact, he was an admitted failure at math in high school. But the show's brilliant writing and integration of real mathematics proved transformative for Krumholtz's perception of the subject. On the extras section of the season 1 DVD, he expresses a beautiful truth about the subject: "There is a spirituality to mathematics that few people understand."

Fifteen years ago, a relatively unknown Hollywood actor with a wholly *unsatisfying* experience with mathematics crystalized a wider domain for studying mathematics, and essentially gave a historical road map to its most prized and accessible reason for exploration—wellness. Specifically, spiritual wellness. On the show, his character used mathematics in a practical manner to solve crimes. In real life, David Krumholtz the person—not the actor—communicated the highest possible purpose for learning mathematics. Tragically, that idea had its most powerful advocate in sickness a hundred years ago.

If you're skeptical of pop cultural references, let me offer another figure whose relationship to mathematics was motivated by the spiritual. In 1920, a frail thirty-three-year-old Indian man from a rural village in Southern India lay on his deathbed. Thanks to the movie

The Man Who Knew Infinity, most of you will know that this person was Srinivasa Ramanujan. Connectedness is a lucky thing to have in our world. Some do not have it or lose it at the end. The spiritual pillar of wellness shows up here in these dark and isolating moments. During that final year of his life, Ramanujan had written 130 pages of notes on scrap paper—and fifty-six years later, the American mathematician George Andrews discovered these notes and compiled them into *Ramanujan's Lost Notebook*, a title that justly hints at the lore that has been afforded to the great thinker. Indian mathematician Richard Askey, a collaborator on this exhaustive project, had this to say about the collection of those notes: "The work of that one year, while he was dying and in considerable pain, was the equivalent of a lifetime of work of a very great mathematician."

But unlike most great mathematicians, Ramanujan was very clearly not studying mathematics for any practical reason. In fact, the applicability of some of his insights would not be fully understood for decades to come. While today, Ramanujan is seen as one of the greatest mathematicians in history, his approach to mathematics—speculative, extrarational, and intuitive—was initially viewed unfavorably by Western eyes. The fact that he attributed so much of his work to divine intervention must have been an affront to those who knew of his work. The following is an excerpt from a blog, "The Secrets of Ramanujan's Garden," that details his religious connection to mathematics:

> While the beauty of the story has long impacted all students of mathematics, the nature of Ramanujan's mathematical genius, and how he himself perceived it, tends to be less explored. Hardy called it some kind of deep "intuition," but Ramanujan openly stated that he received the mathematical inspiration and sometimes whole formulas, through contacting the Hindu Goddess Namagiri while dreaming. Ramanujan was an observant Hindu, adept at dream interpretation and astrology. Growing up, he learned to worship Namagiri, the Hindu Goddess of

creativity. He often understood mathematics and spirituality as one. He felt, for example, that zero represented Absolute Reality, and that infinity represented the many manifestations of that Reality.

> # An equation for me has no meaning unless it expresses a thought of God.
> ## —Srinivasa Ramanujan

As wonderful of a story as that is, there is a more recent one that encapsulates the need for a broader purpose of learning mathematics. This story is about Christopher Jackson.

In early 2020, Francis Su, former president of the Mathematics Association of America, came out with a generational book, a needed primer, on how to live a more fully human life, *Mathematics for Human Flourishing*. The person he chose to illustrate this was Christopher:

> Christopher Jackson is an inmate in a high-security federal prison. He's been in trouble with the law since he was fourteen. He didn't finish high school, he had an addiction to hard drugs, and at age nineteen he was involved in a string of armed robberies that landed him in prison with a thirty-two-year sentence.

If you don't know the story of how a Harvard PhD mathematician came to write this powerfully human book dedicated to his friend Christopher—and opening with such a demoralizing background—then I implore you to seek it out. Ramanujan was incarcerated by the illness of his body. Jackson was incarcerated by the systemic failures of society. Two people from totally different backgrounds and moments in time who sought out mindful and affirming refuge in the world of mathematics. That's right. Christopher, having little hope of having the societal definition of success and happiness, found his *own* purpose for learning mathematics. A death bed and a jail cell. Two of the grimmest situations one could imagine.

And, yet even harder to imagine is that something like mathematics could temper, maybe even ameliorate, the misery of physical and emotional pain, and the dense isolation that it brings. So the bridge between these two people that helps us better understand what gave them and has given them solace lies affirmatively in Krumholtz's quote on mathematics and spirituality. Our collective understanding and appreciation for mathematics should include situations that we pray we never find ourselves in. Yet, at the same time, we know that mathematics can be there to offer comfort if we ever do. We owe it to Ramanujan and Jackson to immerse ourselves in math with more hope, humanity, and higher purpose than is currently done.

There is a widening chasm of connection that is now left for us to cross. We will be incapable of making this trek if we cannot get to the core of our humanity. There is lots of social, emotional, and mathematical pain that needs to be addressed. I believe it starts with stories.

In 2020, I gave a keynote at state math conferences in Pennsylvania, Illinois, and New York. While so many school districts were mired in the false idea of students falling behind, and sadly reminding us all of education's stubborn relationship with its toxic past of pace and performance, I chose to focus on something more binding, hopeful, and respectful of the potential of mathematics in our lives. The title of my keynote was "Storytelling: The Journey of Rehumanizing Mathematics for All."

Take out the word "mathematics" from that title. Every other word is saying "1.0"—a resetting of mathematics that considers its humanity. We are in the throes of creating the first iteration of such a concept. In my keynote, I told two stories about the Agta people, a hunter-gatherer society in the Philippines. One was about the Sun (man) and Moon (woman) having a dispute over who should illuminate the sky. They decided that the Sun should light the day and the moon the night. The purpose of this story was to convey gender equality, that both males and females should equally share important roles in a society. The second story I told was about a wild pig and sea cow that would race every day on land, until one day the sea cow hurt its legs. The wild pig picked up the sea cow and took it to the ocean, where they continued to race. The wild pig on land and the sea cow in the water. The purpose of this story was to promote friendship, cooperation, empathy, and an aversion to inequality.

The survival and happiness of these societies depend on a collectivist mindset. Many countries in Asia, Africa, and South America tend to adopt this philosophy. Most countries in Europe and North America live off the idea of the individual. There is only one thing left that can save us as a society from becoming even more alienated from each other and anchor the future of education: our humanity. It fuels and gives life to a more collectivist idea of learning. Equality, equity, kindness, empathy, and generosity are inextricably braided into building a mathematical culture of collectivism. The tears that fell from John Conway's eyes at the thought of the first meeting of the International Congress of Mathematicians is the symbolic plea for a mathematics that is best when it is shared with everyone. We have stared long enough into this abyss. We have what we need here. Time to move on. It's time to search for a bridge.

LOST BRIDGES

Never to forget where we came from and always
praise the bridges that carried us over.
—Fannie Lou Hamer

Planting the seed about being *lost together* at end of the first chapter was kind of mandatory. I mean, we aren't chasing rabbits in a fenced-off petting zoo. It's more like a forest. Except this forest is big. Really big. So much so, that we have no idea how big. No, seriously, we don't. So, getting lost is inevitable—and remember, that is a good thing! The fact that we are all lost and chasing levels the playing field. Being lost and admitting we are lost is a vulnerable position. Harnessing that, trying to find ourselves and answer the big questions in life will bring more patience and possibilities. Having comfort in new situations, new problems, and new adventures is part of strengthening the mental pillar of wellness. Yet we have lost the idea of being lost. In a short blog post, photographer and artist Laura Valenti offers this soulful reflection on the currency of being lost: "We know where we are just about all the time now. Even worse, we think we SHOULD know where we are all the time. So, being lost feels like a real problem when it happens."

Imagine the anxiety of uploading this idea into learning mathematics. Well, we don't need to imagine it. This is the reality of probably every student of mathematics. Literally, there is no time to be lost. Valenti then goes on to point out the sad inevitability in depriving oxygen to the idea of being lost:

> This kind of thinking impacts the creative process, too. We expect to know exactly what we're doing at all times. Our next steps as artists shouldn't be a mystery. We think we're failing if we don't see a clear path forward. This is causing a lot of artists a lot of pain. Because, being lost is a place of possibility, adventure, receptivity, and . . . creativity. Having everything figured out at the outset? Or, thinking you do? That's like putting blinders on.

Preventing being lost in mathematics is pretty much ignoring the history of mathematics and its thematic development. Take away being lost, and you've obliterated many of math's most endearing stories.

95

However, while our society typically upholds a firm grip on accurate orientation over the mysteries of being lost, the notion of "lostness" has long fascinated our collective imagination. Perhaps the most famous example is the lost city of Atlantis, a story told by Plato in 360 BCE. And while nobody believes that this city, which supposedly existed nine thousand years before Plato's time, was real, its legend has not been dampened over time. As a child of the '70s, I badly wanted to believe in the existence of such a fabled city of half-god/half-human beings. The word *lost* resonates so powerfully with our psyches, implying that something of immense value and mystery could be housed there.

Twentieth-century pop culture focuses most often on stories about humans who are lost. In the '60s, it was the show *Lost in Space*. In the '70s, it was the Saturday morning show *Land of the Lost* (the Will Ferrell movie remake almost ruined my memories of this show). And, as previously mentioned, *Lost*, one of the most popular and heavily analyzed shows of all time, became a hotbed for conversation for six years, from 2004 to 2010. The characters' state of being lost heightened all their most human emotions and desires: purpose, meaning, connection, and love.

Beginning with a philosophy of lostness invites a temperament for learning mathematics that is honest, affirming, and healthy. Yet, the proclamation of being lost in a mathematics classroom has negative connotations—you are at risk of falling behind in the *race to learn*. Sadly, that mentality is still prevalent more than ten years after director Vicki Abeles's documentary *Race to Nowhere*, about the educational burnout of children, was released. (We will explore Abeles's third documentary, which might be her best and is germane to the themes of this book, in the next chapter.)

Being comfortable with being lost also means you will have a higher probability of seeing math's awe and wonder. The hero's journey in mathematics, as student or a teacher, begins with this very primer. It is the caterpillar of learning. The butterfly? You might have already guessed that by now: curiosity. (The butterfly also represents something else. That metaphor awaits us at the end of this book—no peeking!)

TO PATTERN OR NOT TO PATTERN

Look at the image below. Without even having instructions, you are probably going to start adding the numbers in each array, which takes on a consistent diamond shape after the first figure. Students will enjoy the adding, even throwing in some multiplication to facilitate the answers. If you ask them what the total will be in the fifth array, I am sure many will enjoy trying to replicate the pattern of numbers that will make mini triangles above and below the "equator" of 5s.

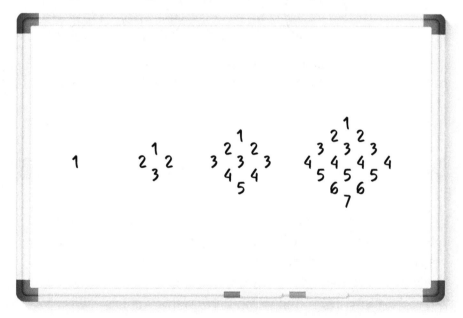

Some careful counting, a recount here and there, and a confident 125 will be offered, soon to reveal the generalization of n^3. A tilted square + sequence of numbers + symmetry = cubes. A wonderful, recognizable pattern that offered up a nice little surprise.

But imagine the surprise that lies in store with a sequence that seems to follow a pattern—until it doesn't! What if we showed the following picture to elementary, middle, and high school students? Some "obvious" patterning seems to be materializing. I wonder how many students will predict that a circle diagram with 6 points will contain 32 regions.

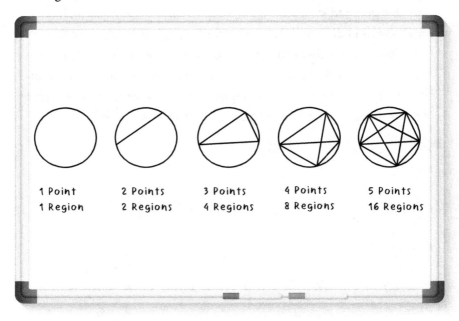

| 1 Point | 2 Points | 3 Points | 4 Points | 5 Points |
| 1 Region | 2 Regions | 4 Regions | 8 Regions | 16 Regions |

When you tell them that 32 is *not* the answer, a collective disbelief will naturally materialize, generating the energy to know what the answer really is, rendering everyone perplexingly, rousingly . . . lost. *What the hell is going on?* they'll wonder, whether or not you reveal that the answer is 31. And telling students that 7 points will produce 57 regions might elicit a sheepish "Is there a pattern going on here?" When everything seems broken and lost is quite often when we fire up the coals of curiosity. Even though 2^n got shot down, curiosity will still demand that the question of patterning stay on the table. Congratulations. You've taken the students to a mathematical rabbit hole. Now it is up to our students to guide the conversation with their questions. Depending on their age, much mathematical deviousness can be revealed. A simple differences chart will invite more curiosity— and the rabbit holes leading to Pascal's triangle and combinatorics, if the requisite knowledge is there.

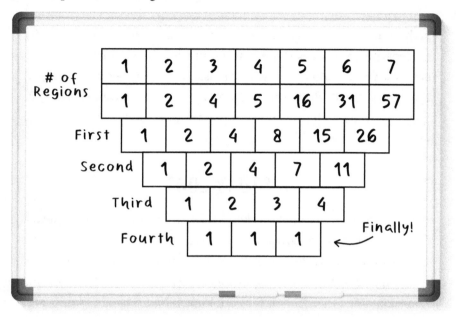

The first row is the diagram number. The second row is the number of regions. The third row is the difference between consecutive values of the row above. These differences are continued until they are "stabilized." If you are a middle school or high school teacher, you might say there is a polynomial equation for how many regions n lines give you. Tell them you forget it, but by just looking at the fourth column you know that this will be a *quartic equation* with a coefficient of 1/24. Mumble something about calculus and derivatives under your breath to add to the burgeoning mystery of this problem. Adding colorful anecdotes gives students an inviting welcome to examine the mathematics. Sometimes it may be confusing, sometimes not. Again, don't worry a great deal about being lost. That is the position we started in. That is the position we will also finish in.

While this problem is rich in mathematical excursion—*and diversions*—it does have a finale to its arithmetic beginnings. For this problem, that termination is a tad complex. But the fact that we want some generalization of the pattern is a testimonial to the power of algebra. Unfortunately, we rarely take students to algebra through its historical path of arithmetic. Algebra feels more like an island. We need to fly students there. It doesn't seem to be part of the landmass of mathematics, vividly connected with thousands of years of development. Essentially, the bridges from arithmetic to algebra have become lost, metaphorically collecting moss along a trail no longer accessed. We need to find them.

A STORY LOST

Around thirty years after Shakespeare penned my favorite tragedy, *King Lear*, René Descartes, one of the most revered minds of the Renaissance era, wrote one of the most important books in modern mathematics—*Discours de la méthode* (*Discourse on Method*). This book contained the symbols for both known (a, b, c) and unknown (x, y, z) quantities in algebra.

This was the first time that a mathematics textbook would resemble the textbooks of today. Unfortunately, the excitement and importance of that event in the *long, long story of algebra*, has been *long, long forgotten*. So much so that algebra is often spoken of derisively now by both students and math educators. The cascade of bitterness has been happening for some time now, with its development brought about by a now (in)famous 2012 article by Andrew Hacker in the *New York Times*.

Hacker's thoughts on algebra can be distilled to its overall practicality for students. Hacker argues through a lens of usefulness and success—hardly things that champion algebra's logistic beauty. And ironically, algebra was rich in application when it began to bloom in the Arab world a thousand years ago. But strangely, I do agree with Hacker. Not that algebra should be easily disposed of, but that algebra in its current state of high school isolation, rife with clichéd explorations and problems, has a declining currency. And as such, does not have the value that it could have. Hacker is correct in getting rid of algebra. But he argues from a point of it being dilapidated. He does not—cannot—envision a resurrection to a richer past through telling its story and illuminating its artistic merits.

Any math story that makes it to mainstream media tends to explore stereotypical ideas of mathematical concern—homework, false ideas perpetuated by Common Core, and of course, the question of *usefulness*. Kids need to do more homework. Common Core is fuzzy math. Algebra is useless. Oh, yes. The mathematical sky is always falling in mainstream media. Kids not knowing their times tables means the space program will be in danger somehow. Going down the utility/practicality road with mathematics is selling it wrong and horribly short—I am still waiting to apply my understanding of *King Lear* to my daily routines of housework, shopping, and raising kids. I can also count the number of times knowing the transition elements of the periodic table or WWI history has bailed me out in my nine-to-five interactions and transactions with society: zero. Learning for practicality is an empty pursuit. You will chase down nothing. Learn for the romance of knowledge. Learn for what woos your heart and soul. Franz Kafka, one of my favorite writers, said it best many years ago: "Don't bend; don't water it down; don't try to make it logical; don't edit your own soul according to the fashion. Rather, follow your most intense obsessions mercilessly." *Mercilessly*. This implies finding your edges. You will not find your edges if you are not willing to get lost. Taking linear paths and linear cues in our progression of teaching and life will not even give us a glimpse of the edges we need to feel and experience. Mathematics is a treasure chest of edges. We need to tell our students about them. Better yet, take them there. *Curiosity* and *identity* are locals. But they are almost impossible to meet if students do not encounter *belonging* in a classroom. I am not talking about belonging in the sense of grade level appropriateness or readiness; those feel more like administrative checklist items for measuring success. They have nothing to do with the humanization of the classroom and of mathematics. The most universal way to create belonging and reach people with gobs of humanness is storytelling. It is such an integral idea to this book that it got its own *magical* chapter.

The problem has never been with algebra per say; it has to do with how it has been incorrectly isolated and rebranded as a course of study reserved for disgruntled and apathetic teenagers. But those gnarly teenage attitudes are not algebra's fault. Imagine if, instead of focusing on useless debates about algebra's pragmatic applications, we told the *story* of algebra, and all those who have stumbled through it with arithmetic and/or patterning. We could center the story on someone students can identify with, a young teenager named Leonardo of Pisa. He was single-handedly responsible for spreading the mathematical genius of Arabic and Hindu scholars like al-Khwarizmi, al-Samaw'al, Omar Khayyam, Aryabhata, and Brahmagupta, to name but a few. That auspicious moment in time is filled with serendipity, historical inflection, and robust practicality, and we will explore it in detail soon!

While we were still hundreds of years away from seeing the familiar algebra of today's textbooks, this period—oddly known as the Dark Ages—would provide one of the most shining moments in algebra's development. This development—*still going on today*—is the main reason we can go deeper and deeper into the mathematical universe and see the existence of numbers and patterns that would otherwise be impossible without algebra.

A BRIDGE NOT TOO FAR

We need to find the lost bridges between arithmetic and algebra. One of the best ones was created by Peter Harrison. My luck in seeing math through this prism of delight is due so much to the wisdom, joy, and passion Peter showered me with over the years, passed down with equal affection by Peter Taylor. Please be pleasantly puzzled and intrigued by the diagram below. Some of you might have seen it—in my last book, *Math Recess: Playful Learning in an Age of Disruption*. I am going to continue that story here.

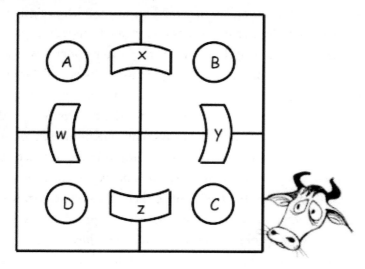

Eight unknowns. Without my even telling you about the relationship between the unknowns, you are *anticipating* one. Do not worry. It is remarkably simple. The "bridges" (w, x, y, and z) represent the sum of adjacent "fields of cows" (A, B, C, and D). For this puzzle, you must enter single digit numbers only, and no digit can be repeated. There are three unique solutions. All can be obtained with even minor brute force, making this problem universally accessible. I have spent years working with Peter's Cows in the Classroom puzzles. I have seen sixth graders gobble up unknowns like gummy bears. There is no intimidation by them. That is because the context is decluttered. There are no silly "real-life" situations that involve algebra's awkward presence. If you cannot make algebra attractive without contrived applications, then it is already game over. Students will sniff out the bullshit of something like finding mystery ages of family numbers with cryptic information from the *ghosts of algebra's past, present, and future*.

Cows. Goofy-looking cows. Bridges. That is a fictitious world. As mentioned previously, many ideas in mathematics would fare better in a fantasy realm than a realistic one. Peter Harrison's "Cows" workshops were his most popular workshops when he taught. He used the same template of cows and bridges to teach addition and subtraction to elementary students and even something as complex as eigenvectors to high school students. Nobody has ever created a more unifying concept of arithmetic and algebra. And even younger students will be able to grasp the nugget of mathematical gold that falls out of this algebra problem—that is saddled with 30 percent of the alphabet's letters!

The numbers 1 to 9 add up to 45. Since there are only eight digits required for a solution, we will always omit one number. Since there are three unique solutions, we will omit three different numbers. *There is a relationship between all three that can only be seen through the lens of algebra.* Add up all the fields. Since there are no like terms, it just becomes one long, seemingly inconsequential expression: $A + B + C + D + w + x + y + z$. Looks daunting and impenetrable.

Or does it? We need to examine individual bridge/field relationships. Look at $A + B$. It equals x! Let's replace that $A + B$ with x in our general expression. We now have $x + C + D + w + x + y + z$. You can see what we will do next: the same thing with the last two capitalized terms. $C + D$ equals z. We now have an equivalent expression with just the lowercase unknowns:

$$x + z + w + x + y + z$$

Hmmm. What do you notice? There are two x's and two z's. With what seems like a third wheel in this expression, $w + y$. Look carefully at w and y. What are they equal to? That is right: $A + D$ and $B + C$, respectively. And isn't the sum of those unknowns equal to $x + z$? There is no third wheel! There are three ways to make those $(x + z)$'s. Which means the original expression can be reduced to $3(x + z)$. Taking it one step deeper, it means that the total will always be a multiple of 3! So, if the digits from 1 to 9 equal 45, which is divisible by three, then the omitted numbers must also be divisible by 3. Case studies of removing

3, 6, and 9 from the playing field now make the problem much easier. There is no need to go further to get the solutions. The spotlight was on the elegance of algebra. Algebra has done its job. Every time I have done this activity with middle school kids, they have all appreciated how the *reason poems* (Paul Lockhart) came into play in this puzzle. It wasn't just logic. It was the *flow* of the logic. It was how the logic of algebra organized *lines of truth* to deliver a satisfying conclusion. The reasoning is simple with an understated elegance. It is not surprising that young students are captivated by the power of algebra. After all, youth and algebra are part of the lore of math history—stay tuned!

MATHEMATICS' TELESCOPE

Antu, Kueyen, Melipal, and Yupen. These are words in the Mapuche language for astronomical objects. They are also the names of the four telescopes that make up the Very Large Telescope (VLT) in northern Chile. The massive optical strength of the telescope with the clarity of the sky in this desert region makes it possible to see stunning things, like the event horizons of black holes, giving humans deeper understanding of the universe. Even as I typed those words, a chill was going through me knowing that I was about to use these telescopes as a metaphor for discussing the power of algebra. *Algebra is the telescope of mathematics.* It has taken a couple of millennia to build. But instead of seeing algebra as a towering art form of mystery and delight, society sees and experiences an algebra that is devoid of story, suspense, and seduction. We need our students to be smitten with the subject. And it all starts with folding in, weaving in, and coloring in the stories, people, achievements, milestones, and mysteries of mathematics, rather than just simply finding x.

Everyone agrees the first *Die Hard* movie is the best of the bunch. And you are thinking: *There is no way I missed any cool algebra in one of the best Christmas movies of all time, right?* No, but in *Die Hard III*, there is a scene where Bruce Willis is channeling, unknowingly, a problem rooted in algebra. Specifically, Diophantine equations. *Whoa, stop! How is Bruce Willis mixed up in* that? There are two empty jugs, a 3-gallon one and a 5-gallon. The challenge in the film is to fill one of the jugs with exactly 4 gallons (*of course it will have to be the 5-gallon one*). Fairly certain you are familiar with the problem either through the movie or from somewhere else. Sure, there is logic in the process of dumping water in and out of the jugs, but there is also . . . algebra!

Now, before getting further into the *Die Hard III* problem, let's talk about what Diophantine equations are. Quite simply, they are equations with two or more unknowns in which only integer solutions are sought or examined. How many ways are there to make change for two dollars using nickels (x) and quarters (y)? Quite a few. Diophantine equations, with their openness, seem to be more inviting in their multiple solutions. It does not take much to generalize our question.

$$5x + 25y = 200$$

To propose solutions, it is easier to factor out the 5 from our equation.

$$x + 5y = 40$$

At this point, all we need to do is get multiples of 5, starting from 0, until we hit 40. They are 0, 5, 10, 15, 20, 25, 30, 35, and 40. Putting these values in will generate the corresponding quarters. So, our full solution of change possibilities is (0, 8), (5, 7), (10, 6), (15, 5), (20, 4), (25, 3), (30, 2), (35, 1), and (40, 0), where the first number represents nickels and the second number quarters. The process we just did is a simplified *Diophantine analysis*. As far as I know, this topic is not even covered in high school.

So, what is "all Diophantine" in *Die Hard III*? It has an elegant algebraic solution! Before exploring this, let's employ the quasi-panic-trial-and-error of John McClane and Zeus Carver, and figure out a solution that way. Here are the steps:

1. Fill the 5-gallon jug. The 3-gallon jug is empty.
2. Empty 3 gallons from the 5-gallon jug into the 3-gallon jug.
3. There remain 2 gallons in the 5-gallon jug. Empty the 3-gallon jug.
4. Pour the 2 gallons into the 3-gallon jug.
5. Fill the 5-gallon jug and pour 1 gallon from it into the 3-gallon jug—filling the 3-gallon jug.
6. Four gallons remain in the 5-gallon jug. Problem solved.

The cachet of this classic problem of course increases by being in a Hollywood movie. As such, every student is going to want to noodle around with jugs, filling and dumping. But not only is there some nifty algebra going on, but there is also some cool number theory—so much intertwining of two of the most important areas of mathematics. But it takes brute force, hard work, and lots of time on the road with the wrong map—or no map at all—to ultimately arrive at the logical elegance of mathematics.

So, after this jug problem is solved with a little bit of sweat, now would be the time to roll out the hidden and historical mathematics. Let's start here:

$$3x + 5y = 4$$

Quickly, you see numbers 3, 4, and 5 from the jug problem, with the 4 representing the required solution. What do you think x and y represent? I wonder if even elementary students could respond by filling/emptying with the 3 and the 5. I think they could. And, if they have the required integer knowledge—*which should start in first grade* (that will be explored later in the book)—they can play around with values to get 4. This is still playful trial and error, but it is now on an algebraic trampoline. Once the solution of x is 3 and y is -1 is tested (which means the 3-gallon jug is *filled three times* and the 5-gallon jug is *emptied once*), the curiosity begins to spiral toward the question—*are there others?* Sure enough, some more math play will reveal a second solution. Students are now at the precipice of fully appreciating what can come next. Primes, lowest common divisor, and the Euclidean algorithm all await to rev up the solution to this problem with a high-performance engine.

Some of the greatest wonders in mathematics occur when algebra dances with number theory. When the two get together, not only is there beauty, but also the telescopic power of algebra becomes quite extraordinary.

$$x^3 + y^3 + z^3 = n$$

Now this cubic equation above might seem ambiguous, maybe even irrelevant. It's not, at least in terms of human ingenuity and perseverance. This is the famous cubes problem posed first back in 1954 at Cambridge University, where mathematicians wondered if there was proof for solutions/nonsolutions to integer values for x, y, and z that can produce the results of n, from 1 to 100. How about we scale back a few dimensions and just do this:

$$x + y + z = 1$$

In this case, it is quick to see there will be infinite solutions for $n = 1$, and for every number after that. The freedom afforded here is an important discussion to have. If we go on to the next dimension, squares, we quickly run into some heavy constraints, since squaring will always give us a positive value, and we will always be adding. As such, there are no solutions for n equals 1 or 2, and we must begin with the following:

$$1^2 + 1^2 + 1^2 = 3$$

Again, the *inflexibility of the situation* can be an important point to throw into our knapsack of mathematical thinking. These subtle changes in conditions bear mentioning. They are small moments, but they have value. To realize that we lose the power to subtract with squared numbers is a wispy moment of mathematical intimacy that we might take for granted. It is like finding a tiny, shiny pebble on our long, lifetime mathematical walk. It's nothing spectacular, but it has some significance, nonetheless. With the boundaries set up by squaring, the search is far more manageable. But who does not love a good challenge! With cubes, it gets to be way more loosey-goosey, and as such, unbounded. Even clever mathematics and super computers can only do so much—time sometimes becomes the final arbiter of when solutions are found.

Up until 2019, every single value for $n = 1$ to 100 was found, except for 33 and 42. Some quirky ways to harness the needed computational power and high school algebra eventually allowed for the final two results to emerge. The solution for 33 was found in 2019 by Andrew Booker. Which meant fans of *The Hitchhiker's Guide to the Galaxy* would mythologize the number 42 even more, as 42 is seen as the answer to "everything" in the book. However, solving for 42 posed another level of complexity. The following is excerpted from an article published by the University of Bristol, where Andrew Booker is a professor:

> Professor Booker turned to MIT mathematics professor Andrew Sutherland, a world record breaker with massively parallel computations, and—as if by further cosmic coincidence—secured the services of a planetary computing platform reminiscent of "Deep Thought," the giant machine which gives the answer 42 in *Hitchhiker's Guide to the Galaxy*. Booker and Sutherland's solution for

42 would be found by using Charity Engine, which is a "worldwide computer" that harnesses idle, unused computing power from over half a million home PCs to create a crowd-sourced, super-green platform made entirely from otherwise wasted capacity.

$$42 =$$
$$(-80538738812075974)^3$$
$$+80435758145817515^3$$
$$+12602123297335631^3$$

Look at the size of these numbers. Look at where they occur on the number line, and then get cubed, and when all is shaken out with addition and subtraction, we get a relatively scrawny two-digit number. For me, this feels like finding planets in another galaxy—after a long, long journey involving lots of wrong turns. I know they are just numbers, but there is something oddly reassuring about knowing that the sum of cubes problem for numbers from 1 to 100 can be put to bed. But there is a discovery that utilizes the language of algebra that I think is even more gob smacking than this in terms of its existence and level of surprise.

A PATTERN GOES TO SLEEP

The more basic a problem, the sooner it can be completely and clearly understood by the widest audience. At which it can be more alluring to learn that its luminosity is rooted in the deepest mysteries of mathematics. Look at the Pythagorean theorem, a staple of middle school mathematics, elevated into pop culture as one of those relationships that everyone just knows. It's also the foundation for Fermat's last theorem. Infinite solutions for the exponent 2, zilch for every number thereafter. Case closed. Except Fermat's enigma, which sat unsolved for three and a half centuries, was a cold case—a very, very cold case. That is an extremely long time, even in the slothlike timelines of mathematical discoveries.

Now, understanding right angles and the algebraic relationships of their sides might be a bit much for young children, like those in first grade. But what about another problem that, like my lesson on perfect numbers, is couched in number theory—and, like that dynamic lesson, offers students an element of tactile play? This time, let's replace the Unifix cubes with four red Lego Duplo blocks. That is how Dr. Jamie Grimes of Numberphile fame introduced this problem, which offers a blazing example of the distance between how basic a mathematical problem can start off and the unimaginable realms where it may end up. We are going to look again to Ramanujan, and his partitions.

Partitioning. Sounds kind of technical, but it's actually quite an intuitive quality of playing with blocks, in that you pull them apart and put them back together again. Students playing randomly with a tower of four blocks will probably even uncover the answer *before* the question is posed. The question? *How many ways can you break down a number into its positive parts*? Well, with 4, here are the answers.

$$4 = 4$$
$$4 = 3 + 1$$
$$4 = 2 + 2$$
$$4 = 2 + 1 + 1$$
$$4 = 1 + 1 + 1 + 1$$

Five ways. Single-digit addition. All possibilities accounted for. Nodding and smiling faces from the first graders. And you know at least one of them, if given this problem, will suggest doing it with 5. But maybe we should go back and do 1, 2, and 3. Here are the partitions for numbers from 1 to 10 then.

Integer	Partitions
1	1
2	2
3	3
4	5
5	7
6	11
7	15
8	22
9	30
10	42

I wonder when the fatigue of doing these by hand might set in? For younger kids, this might be a fun exercise in practicing their "addition tables"! But, at some point, it's no longer interesting, especially if there is nothing to be revealed. Sure, kids might be interested in a familiar milestone number like a hundred, but interest will dry up. Younger people are generally more curious, so don't be surprised if someone asks how we figured out the partitions for 100. And, if someone does, get a little bit cryptic and cue up a video of a Formula 1 race car. Now we can talk about algebra. You see, not all heroes wear capes.

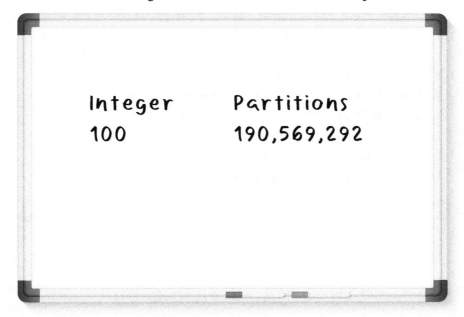

Integer   Partitions
100   190,569,292

Is there a formula to "plug into" and churn out these partition numbers? Sure enough, there is! If you have never seen it before, it's going to mess with your head. And Ramanujan was who tackled this problem to find it. However, some of the early work had already been done by the great mathematician Euler.

What Ramanujan saw—what the timeline was will always be a mystery; how long did it take for this mathematical epiphany to come to him?—is that the partitions appeared to have *structure*. It's like he was seeing the *lattice structure* of these numbers much like a chemist or physicist might see all the structural bonds and relationships between atoms. There was order, but maybe only a mathematician of Ramanujan's caliber could find it. He also did not need a high-powered optical instrument. He had one preinstalled. For example, he realized that the partitions for all numbers in the form $5n + 4$ (where n is greater than or equal to 0) were divisible by 5. Let's check our short list to see if this holds true. If we make $n = 0$, then we are left with 4, and sure enough, there are five ways to partition 4. If we make $n = 1$, we get $5 + 4 = 9$. That number has thirty partitions. These are things we could easily share with students to make them "curiouser and curiouser" about what is going on here. With one observation might come a demand for more. As educators, that's what we want from our students. Insistence. Which occurs when we give them a captivating and accessible problem, along with the history and our own playful narrative. A byproduct of the problem at hand, and nothing else.

Sure enough, Ramanujan found even more divisibility relationships. Here they are (P stands for "partition"):

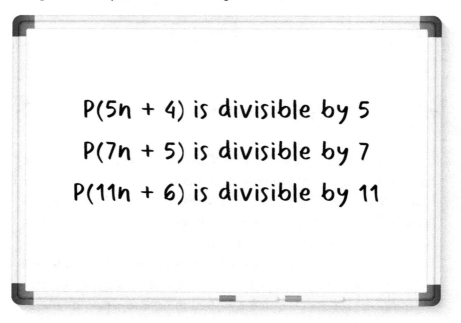

$P(5n + 4)$ is divisible by 5

$P(7n + 5)$ is divisible by 7

$P(11n + 6)$ is divisible by 11

This is one of those rare moments in mathematics. Before we get to the next partition divisibility rule, we should stop. Because what happens next is a combination of the telescopic powers of mathematics, and also of the subtle, dark romanticism that is always lurking around it. There is patterning going in these three definitive relationships that is accessible to all. It would not be very hard for almost anyone to take a stab at the next partition rule: $P(13n + 7)$ is divisible by 13, for the next prime number in the bracket would be 13 and the next number after 6 is 7. Finally, the divisibility number we would test is also the next prime after 11: 13.

The problem is more than that it is incorrect. The problem is that it is ridiculously incorrect. It is like expecting to find another planet at a certain distance from a newfound star and it's not there. You keep looking around in a pretty generous radius from that star, but nothing. You give up and come to the conclusion that those we already know are the only planets tied to this star.

Even the brilliant Ramanujan didn't have the mathematical power to find the next partition formula. Half a century later, however, mathematicians found this:

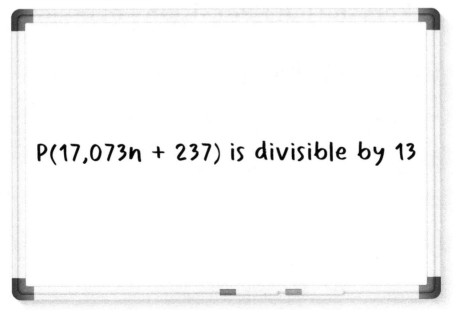

$$P(17{,}073n + 237) \text{ is divisible by } 13$$

That unimaginable *silence* between partition formulas for divisibility by 11 and 13 is, for me, where the magnificence of mathematics lies—its simple and beautiful ability to surprise. If the formulas ceased to exist past the first three, then that would leave us with some mild bemusement in a rather short algebraic story. *But hundreds of blank pages later, the story continues.* Imagine thinking that there definitely has to be a planet where Venus is located, given the locations of Mercury, Mars, and Earth. But there isn't. Instead, it is merrily sitting out in the heliopause like it belongs there. Just like the divisibility rules for prime numbers and partitions. While this is all nice and wonderfully weird—I wish we would spotlight math's quirks and absurdities much more often—we still haven't got that magic formula that figures out the number of partitions for any number we select. Well, Ramanujan and Hardy came up with one. It looks like something that would be used in a mathematical meme to scare people about mathematics. Truth be told, yeah, it's a bit daunting.

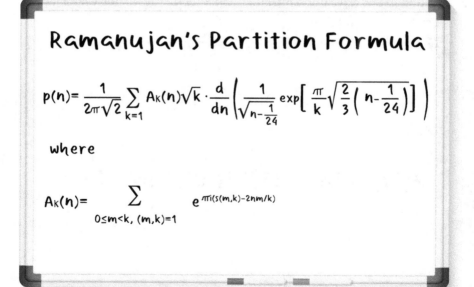

Ramanujan's Partition Formula

$$p(n) = \frac{1}{2\pi\sqrt{2}} \sum_{k=1} A_k(n)\sqrt{k} \cdot \frac{d}{dn}\left(\frac{1}{\sqrt{n-\frac{1}{24}}} \exp\left[\frac{\pi}{k}\sqrt{\frac{2}{3}\left(n-\frac{1}{24}\right)}\right]\right)$$

where

$$A_k(n) = \sum_{0 \leq m < k,\ (m,k)=1} e^{\pi i(s(m,k)-2nm/k)}$$

But remember where we came from! We started with Duplo blocks and results wholly obtainable and understandable by our youngest mathematicians. That formula above, while totally incomprehensible, becomes lodged in the minds of students as a reminder that mystery and magic are abundant in mathematics, and this happens because it was the surprise ending to this mathematical story. Not all stories in math need a final understanding. That simple faith in mathematics, specifically algebra here, reassures us that there is a hidden order to our universe, and that we are never going to uncover all the secrets. We just chase them. Slowly. In circles. One at a time. Let's continue to get lost, *with* algebra as our traveling companion.

6

LIVE TO MATH

I wanted kicks—the kind of melodramatic thrills and chills I'd yearned for since childhood, the kind of adventure I'd found as a little boy in the pages of my Tintin *comic books.*
—Anthony Bourdain

When I was a kid, discussions about food were rooted in the joyless idea that we eat to live, end of story. Food was partitioned into its groups, calories were attributed to proteins, fats, and carbohydrates, and serving sizes and portions all followed from this formula. I think I even wore a shirt in the '70s that sponsored this idea. It was a shirt that had four uninspiring squares, representing the four food groups. The colors of the shirt were beige and brown. They were given out for free to all students to promote healthy eating. Considering how often I chucked my soggy tomato, lettuce, cheese, and ham sandwich into the garbage—apologies to my mother—for cafeteria fries, that nutrition campaign had little impact on me.

Given the psychedelic food abominations of the time, as well—like *tuna and Jell-O casserole*—how food was presented to us as middle school students was rather boring. Nowhere was there ever room to discuss the feeling of biting into a cold, crisp Granny Smith, having that first sip of a homemade chicken noodle soup, or trying to convey the emotions we feel when smelling fresh herbs—many of my happy memories of childhood are anchored to the smell of the leaves of tomato plants in my mother's garden!

Similarly, when it comes to math, of course you need the basics— but utility is still seen as the be all, end all. We're never encouraged to color our learning of math with sensory experiences or emotions— unless you count red crayons for anger or gray ones for sadness. It's as if long division is pulled from the same practicality basket that holds B vitamins. But has anybody ever asked when will we "use" B vitamins in our day-to-day lives? There simply are few adventures students experience with mathematics. As such, any organic celebrations within it are nonexistent.

Okay, how about this: What does math smell like? Did I just ask about the *smell* of . . . math? In loose, romantic terms, I suppose anytime I smell flowers that have symmetry and patterning of numbers in the form 2, 3, 5, 8, 13, 21, 34, etc., I am smelling math, right? (I did not name that familiar sequence for no reason . . .) But allow me to be less romantic and more literal about mathematics, food, and smell. Specifically, how there is math behind . . . curry!

I might be biased, but the greatest cuisine in the world is Indian. The smell of curry is intoxicating for many. It has not only an aromatic power, but a social power to change mindsets regarding race. The history of the British and curry goes back hundreds of years, and it is quite complex. The Brits had a strong affinity for it going back to the early nineteenth century. However, in 1857, when Indian soldiers rebelled against British rule in India, curry fell out of favor—and did not recover until after World War II. The smell of curry became entangled with racism. But today, Indian cuisine is a source of national pride in the UK, and chicken tikka masala is recognized as the national dish. What is it about the combination of spices that elicits such passion for this food? Math—#surprised not surprised, right?

When we think of tasty dishes, we are thinking of ingredients that have similar flavor profiles, like onion and garlic. But, onion even shares some similarity with something like coconut. Think of ingredients like ovals of a Venn diagram. The more they overlap, the more flavor compounds they share. As ingredients become more dissimilar, the shared region of their flavor profile shrinks—but there is still some overlap!

If we focus on the overlapping region, most dishes from Western cuisine, which is generally free of a lot of spices, have lots of overlap. Indian dishes, as you can now probably guess, do not. This is what creates that "wow" in your mouth—especially those tasting them for the first time! Mathematics is literally delicious as well. We should stop being surprised at where, when, and how it shows up to explain the beautiful mysteries of life. Then again, we should not. Let us have both in this life!

Both food and math need to be celebrated with the unifying dazzle and color of curry. But education turns both food and math into a dry discourse that focuses primarily on familiar and tired creations. *So, do we really get to taste math*? In school, the answer is no. Our experiences would dictate that mathematics has been a rather bland tour. If you want to see what a lavish buffet of mathematics looks like, stop reading and go the dazzling world of Mathigon (www.mathigon.org), a free resource for students and teachers.

THE GOOD LIFE

Memories. They are postcards we send ourselves from our sometimes-murky past. My earliest memory of math that stirs something native inside of me is from 1972, when we moved into our first home in Canada. The house was built in 1964, and we were going to be its second occupants. In what would become my bedroom, I found, sitting in the top of the closet, a hardcover book with *Mathematics 12* printed on its gold-and-black spine. It had the wonderful "old book" smell so many of us love. I had just finished grade 2. Like almost all kids around that age, I was fascinated by numbers. Flipping through this book, seeing weird symbols, notations, and text, I remember seeing so many brackets. I did not know what a bracket was at that point, and the presence of something so unfamiliar fortified the idea that mathematics would always hold this seductive mystery for me. How these events occur are often inexplicable. Unfortunately, too many students have memories of mathematics that are, to be frank, benign at best. At worst? Traumatic.

> ## I do not see how it's doing society any good to have so many members walking around with vague memories of algebraic formulas and geometric diagrams and clear memories of hating them.
> ### —Paul Lockhart

The education domain of learning is often written as K to 20 by progressive educators. If mathematics—and all subjects—was taught and showcased in a healthier light, then we could easily proclaim that our learning should extend far beyond our immersion in formal education. Imagine twenty years of positive memories. Curiosity would live well—and live *well*—beyond the space and past the time of classrooms. I can tell you that it takes a lifetime to *appreciate* mathematics—knowns and unknowns, certainties and uncertainties, and solved and unsolved. All those become a hearty dish of memories. We need these memories to emerge and arise variously *over time* within our math world. They can't be rushed. Mathematics is risotto—so stir often!

One of the things that contributes to math's sterility is that after it is extricated from our lives and introduced to us as something alien—that may not be the intention, but that is how it is *received*—we then try to reintroduce it back into our lives and try to give it purpose and meaning through a narrow lens of school's purpose. Mathematics arrives, unsurprisingly, closed and fully discovered. If it were food, it would all be found in the frozen-food section. We have compartmentalized the hell out of it. If you can tell me what deserves to be a grade 5 topic versus a grade 4 topic, I am all ears.

Here's another way of putting it: we need to experience math not as an appendage of life, something only worth its utility as defined within a narrow frame of educational purpose, but as the circulatory system of life. It runs through everything. Its pulse can be felt everywhere. All our hobbies, interests, pastimes, and passions are—or should be—intertwined with mathematics. When I met Anthony Bourdain in Toronto in 2005, for a book signing of *Les Halles*, his French cookbook, I flipped through the introduction as I waited with the roughly few hundred people who had come out to see him. I found this passage near the end, which resonated with me on a pretty deep level: "Do not be afraid. You will need a pure heart, and a soul, meaning you are cooking for the right reasons. You need passion, curiosity, and a full spectrum of appetites. You need to yearn for things. Chef's appetites and enthusiasms, as you have noticed, rarely end at food. I am deeply suspicious of any cook who is less than enthusiastic as well as about sex, music, movies, travel—and LIFE."

Substitute "mathematician" for "cook," and it could have been me writing! My admiration for Anthony Bourdain is well established by now: I quoted him in my first book, *Pi of Life: The Hidden Happiness of Mathematics*, and, in my second book, *Math Recess*, I dedicated a section to him. Now, as he is so regrettably no longer with us, I offer this entire chapter as one last testimonial to his legacy, which I can sum up in a few powerful words: his entire life was *live to*—to eat, to connect, to share.

Add the binding agent of storytelling, and we get the full value of life's mysteries, myths, and memories. Bourdain raised the currency on these things through his affable and honest narrative. It wasn't always pretty, but it was genuine and heartfelt.

Our math memories have been historically negative, with detrimental emotional residue. We have not traveled in the wilderness of mathematics. It's mostly been depressing tourist traps. If students have not experienced math problems that take several days or even a week to solve by the time they get to high school, then they have probably spent their entire career as disappointed tourists.

That is because math has been limited to a *nutrition course*, and not allowed to be a *cooking course*. The courage and curiosity to truly make math a lifetime pursuit lies in yesterday's memories. And those memories should run the spectrum of all the emotions that are housed inside of us. Our reactions to our mathematical world must originate from a place of uncompromising honesty and vulnerability. Often, we will be confused. But it is in this affirming and binding haze that we find the heart and humanness of mathematics.

> # As a cook, tastes and smells are my memories, and I'm in search of some new ones. So I'm leaving New York and hoping to have a few epiphanies around the world. I'm looking for extremes of emotion and experience. I'll try anything. I'll risk everything. I have nothing to lose.
> —Anthony Bourdain, *A Cook's Tour*

Are we in search of new mathematical memories? Not just trying new pedagogical ideas, but experiencing new mathematical content? Our block for being lost, confused, uncertain, or in fear of failure should, hopefully, by now not exist. Every mathematician has been spurred on by *I'll try anything. I'll risk everything. I have nothing to lose.*

Math education, on the other hand, has been all about *math to live.* By this I mean that we've been told to use and understand math to help with the functionality of day-to-day life, maximize its utility, and even stretch it into a career. It's all directed outward, toward anything from survival skills to parlaying it into being something like an actuary or an engineer. That is the *visible spectrum* of math's importance. But math's existence in our universe goes beyond what we can see—and, maybe, what we want to see and experience. Yes, we can use math as a powerful tool. But we can also use math as a balm, a meditative diversion, and a window into the soul of the universe. With possibilities like that, why wouldn't we *live to math*?

For an example of what this might look like, we can turn to Martin Gardner, whose entire mathematical existence—and publication of over a hundred books—did not lie in the domain of practicality. His Mathematical Games columns, which started appearing in *Scientific American* in 1957, have now become legendary. His approach to writing and love of mathematics were firmly seated in his own uncertain ability in mathematics. This is wonderfully captured in this reflection found in his book *Undiluted Hocus-Pocus*:

> One of the pleasures in writing the column was that it introduced me to so many top mathematicians, which of course I was not. Their contributions to my column were far superior to anything I could write and were a major reason for the column's growing popularity. The secret of its success was a direct result of my ignorance. Even today my knowledge of math extends only through calculus, and even calculus I only dimly comprehend. As a result, I had to struggle to understand what I wrote, and this helped me write in ways that others could understand.

The mathematical establishment dubbed his work "recreational," a somewhat backhanded compliment if you ask me. Regardless, Gardner did it right. He gave us blueprints, maps, and guides to the good life—*the good mathematical life.*

These ideas about reevaluating our focus on practicality and purpose are on trend with some broader contemporary societal trends. Last year, I came across a blog by Joanna Bloor titled "Having a Career Path Is Obsolete." Almost immediately, my pop-culture obsessed brain rewound the clock back to 1961 and the *Twilight Zone* episode "The Obsolete Man," starring Burgess Meredith. His character, Romney Wordsworth, is a librarian, and since books have been eliminated, he is deemed obsolete by the totalitarian state. This obsolescence is seen as necessary for the health of a fictional dystopian society. The obsolescence in Bloor's article refers to our health, the individual. Instead of something like *choose your career,* she offers that we should expand that to *choose your adventure.* This feels more like living the good life. This feels more like mathematics.

ARE YOU EXPERIENCED?

One of the key ways that we allow math to saturate our existence is to open ourselves up to the connections between mathematics and our other interests. For me, the strongest pairing with math has always come through music. And, oddly enough, it's not just me—anytime I see a passionate math teacher, they usually maintain a deep, intense, and personal connection to music, as well.

Maybe because music and math share similar journeys. That is not accurate. More like math and music *could* share similar journeys. Most people *could* fall in love with math like music. But they don't. The roads diverge quickly. There is a larger group of people who hate math and love music. It shouldn't be that way at all. Maybe because music is optional, and math is required. Yet both are equally essential and beneficial. I would even say both are sacred. You also don't even have to have any talent (remember Vonnegut's wisdom from the introduction) to have a lifetime love affair with music. Of course, having it amplifies devotion, but you don't need it. And really, should talent and ability be guides for chiseling out our identity? With math, historically, the answer is a lamentable yes. Mathematics should instead follow the trail of the arts—for the simple and ironic reason of mathematicians being able to see many parallels with the arts.

I loved music right from the beginning. But I couldn't appreciate its value until I had logged about thirty years of going to concerts and collecting music. It's taken the same period of time to let the experience of thousands of hours of teaching, memories of thousands of students, and ensnarement by thousands of math problems to produce the same deep appreciation. I have never stopped finding new music—of any genre. The exact same can be said for mathematics. Many of the ideas I am sharing in this book are recent finds. My own bookshelf had maybe only a few math books on it two decades ago. Now I have more than a few hundred. I open up new math books with the same enthusiasm as when I open up newly purchased albums.

Some of the ideas in my math books are tiny. Some are large. Some are solved. Some are unsolved. I digest music the same way. Sometimes I need to listen to a whole album, and sometimes just a song will do. Then, there are even more specific moments when a riff, a bridge, or a lyric can consume me—much like thinking about the mystery that always lurks in a problem like 0/0. There is even a deeper and more specific trench that I would like to explore with you. Below are all the genres of music that iTunes recognizes in my collection—there is even some marked as unclassifiable!

Alternative. Alternative and Punk. Art Rock. Ballad. Blues. Books and Spoken. Celtic Irish Punk Drunk Singing. Celtic Rock. Children's Music. Classic Rock. Classical. Comedy. Country. Country and Folk. Death Metal. Default. Disco. Easy Listening. Electronica. Electronica/ Dance. Folk. General Rock. Genre. Hard Rock. Hip-Hop. Hip-Hop/ Rap. Holiday. Indie Rock. Industrial. Jazz. Latin. Metal. Misc. MST. New Age. Oldies. Other. Polsk Punk. Pop. Progressive Rock. Psychedelic. Punk. R&B. Rap. RAWK. Reggae. Retro. Rock. Rock and Roll. Rock/Pop. Soundtrack. Space. Stoner Rock. Unclassifiable. Unknown. World. 1970s.

I listen to everything. I don't possess the phrase that goes like, "I like all kinds of music except . . ." And I would say the genre of music that has been a primary gateway to everything in life has been hard rock/metal (even though I despise such classification). Thankfully, we have some research that could explain what is going on here. There have been many articles over the last decade or so that point to those who have grown up with the heavy, crushing landscapes of this music being some of the happiest people on the planet. And the healthiest.

Health benefits for fans? Absolutely. In fact, this heavy rudder has been—setting up another irony—a steadfast influence in bringing out the gentler qualities of my personality and those of my friends. So many of the friends I have met along this journey are wonderfully kind, giving, and reflective. I have seen and participated in those mental health benefits for most of my life. But how is this tied to math?

Around late December of 2020, I finally touched base with a kindred spirit, Nikki Rohlfing, who lives in England and used to be a roadie for many heavy metal bands, with a Zoom call. Now he teaches upper-level mathematics in York, a beautiful medieval city in northeast England. We had no agenda. We just knew the conversations would swirl aimlessly between math and music. After finding other friends who live happily ever after in this intersection of heavy joys, I came to some warming conclusions:

Openness, fearlessness, and boundlessness. Most metal fans I know listen to a variety of music as a result of the vast landscape of emotions they experience when listening to bands like Black Sabbath and Iron Maiden. Also, we keep looking and listening for new sounds and bands. We are open to anything and everything. This exact mindset happens in mathematics. We love to explore and continue to explore mathematics that goes beyond the domain of K to 12. Everything that I have learned in the realm of math history and storytelling has come from beyond the mainstream ideas of mathematics found in education.

The rebellious nature found in fans of heavy music becomes a foundation for taking that antiestablishment ethos *everywhere*—including the world of math education. Which explains why I am passionate about the stories of mathematics as much as the mathematics itself. I don't even have a fraction of the résumé of John Conway to have the kinds of stories that could eclipse the mathematics. I am okay with them having equal value in this life.

Colorful micro- and macroprisms of exploration. When Nikki and I were talking about music, we discussed everything from the smallest details, like riffs and down-tuning, to whole album catalogues of bands, to the entire experience of seeing live metal shows with kindred spirits. When Nikki and I were talking about mathematics, we discussed microdetails in problem solving—key algebraic and geometric insights that illuminate paths for solutions—to some of our favorite math problems in algebra and calculus, to the broader joy and passion that mathematics brings to our lives. Those conversations were organic and enthusiastic.

Collectivism, loyalty, and equity. The mathematics communities that I am a part of are very tightly knit. How could they not be, weaving together the joys of math and teaching? As someone who has seen hundreds of hard rock/heavy metal shows over the last four decades, the idea of collectivism and the importance of gathering to share the music is quite easily the most life-affirming result. No other genre of music comes close to the intimate and welcoming vibes. Being *different* is cool. I don't have long hair. I don't have tattoos. I don't have piercings. I am brown. But I often feel most at home with my friends who look like bikers. We are bonding because of what we believe in, not what we look like. I have never seen a wider array of people than at metal concerts—the music of the people for the people.

LIV FOR MATH

Luckily, there is a luminous personality who is the embodiment of the magical alchemy that occurs when the worlds of mathematics and metal collide. Where all the points listed above live and breathe with feral abandonment. Her name is Liv Boeree. Physicist, professional poker player, TEDx speaker, heavy metal guitarist, and nature lover. She's had birthday cakes with math themes, like the quirky phoenix number—the repeating digits of 142857 you get when you divide a nonmultiple of seven by seven—glowing with dyed fondant icing. She has worn Metallica shirts in poker tournaments. She has given wonderful talks in smart business attire.

However, there is another quality about Boeree that I purposely omitted. Perhaps because it might be the most important one—even for the purposes of this book. Philanthropy. Remember how I mentioned that kindness and giving are strong traits intertwined with heavy music? Well, Boeree takes it to the next level and is making generosity a needed attribute for our future. While playing poker—and effectively using her deep mathematical skills—she came across the idea of something called "effective altruism." The belief is rooted in trying to reduce suffering in the world with the resources that are available in always the most effective way. She cofounded Raising for Effective Giving (REG) with other poker players to maximize the impact of charities and research foundations. Liv Boeree has credited her physics degree with giving her this gift of deep analysis, which she has parlayed not only into a successful poker career, but also her analytical instincts, built through a prism of life experiences, and seeing charity with logical clarity and conviction.

An implicit theme in wellness is to not only take care of yourself, but also the world that you live in. I would find it impossible to spend so much holistic attention on myself, but discard the world I inhabit. In fact, if anything, attending to all the pillars of wellness most likely makes you more aware and sensitive to the plight of our planet—the environment, poverty, disease, and so on. For me, Liv Boeree is a role model for bringing personal passion to mathematics and the sciences and to personal and global wellness. I am sure the fusion of math and metal have supported her altruism in ways that are both explicable and inexplicable. As it should be.

We need to mix the colors of mathematics with both the ordinary and extraordinary moments and events of our lives. Nobody can ever be satiated by this connection. Seeing life through and with the beauty of mathematics can only lead to a life well led. And we also need others to help us connect math to things our eyes and experiences may have missed. Around every corner, there is a piece of mathematics to amuse us—sometimes literally.

THE SOFA PROBLEM

When I reflect on how I talk about, share, and teach mathematics now as opposed to when I haphazardly started my career twenty-five years ago, over a Labor Day camping trip, the two are markedly different. It's like I went into a parallel universe—filled with magically human intersections of mathematics. Sure, I am still serious about mathematics, but in terms of my speech and facial expressions, my output is joyful, animated, and even silly at times—especially if we look to *silly*'s Old English/German roots, when the word simply meant "happy." In fact, the modern German word *selig*, which itself is part of the evolutionary development of *silly*, means "extremely overjoyed." Yup. That's me and mathematics in this new decade! And I am letting my other passions whimsically spill all over my love for this subject.

The way that I show math to my kids, my online students, and friends is the same way I would share food recipes, music, and Netflix shows. *This is the BEST chocolate chip cookie recipe! Pearl Jam's first album is a masterpiece of capturing Gen X angst. You need to watch Ricky Gervais's* After Life! *The sofa math problem is bloody beautiful . . .*

What problem? While the sofa math problem is interesting in itself—I mean, Numberphile making a video about it is pretty cool—sharing it with a vigor aligned to *live for math* only occurs because of its perfect intersection with pop culture and our own memorable experiences. Who hasn't moved furniture up and down stairs and around daunting corners? Friendships have been tested through conflicting strategies and strained backs. These are memories of timeless exasperation, sprinkled with sarcasm, jabs of frustration, and whittling patience.

And it was all humorously captured in an episode of the popular show *The Big Bang Theory* when the characters Sheldon and Leonard try to move a furniture box up the stairs because the elevator is out of order. There are some self-deprecating remarks about lacking the physical strength for the job, optimistically offset by claims that the answer lay in "physics." In fact, as the heavy, rectangular box falls flat on the stairs, Leonard and Sheldon engage in some scientific banter:

> Leonard: "The force required to lift is reduced by the sine of the angle of the stairs, call it thirty degrees. So about half."
> Sheldon: "Exactly half."

What's interesting is that the mathematics is pretty bang on (pardon the pun), as the optimum incline of a staircase in a dwelling is between 23 and 37 degrees. Any less, and it would take up more room and start to resemble a ramp. Any more, it starts to become a ladder. Once the box is laid flat and pushed up against the stairs, with some labored breaths, this quick exchange occurs:

> Leonard: "It's all in the math."
> Sheldon: "What's your formula for the corner?"
> Leonard: "Whaat?"

Oh yes. The dreaded corner. Where sofas go to die (or at least gouge out chunks of drywall). Mathematics and friendships tend to be on thin ice at this point. But, as it turns out, there is some heavy-duty algebra to answer Sheldon's sarcastic question—I wonder if the writers of the show were even aware of the sofa problem?

Here it is: What is the maximum area a sofa can have to move around a corner that has a hallway width of one unit? (It is easier to work with the number 1 than an actual hallway width.) What is so charming and mathematically *decadent* about this problem is that we can approach and unpack it with head-nodding simplicity. Make the sofa a unit square. Let that be your first attempt for the biggest sofa (area equals 1) that can be moved around the corner. Our situation will resemble the diagram below.

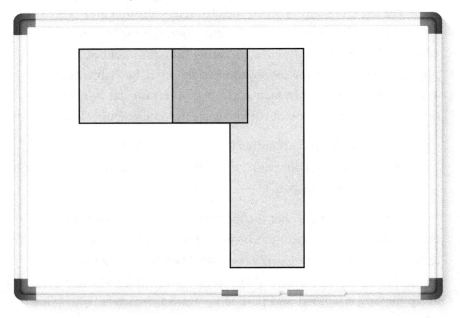

This square moves around the corner by *translation*. Maybe we need a sofa shape that has some *rotational* flexibility? I can see most kids suggesting something that is round or curvy. A circle with radius 1 will have an area of 3.14 units^2. But our sofa would be a semicircle, so our area will be 1.57 units^2. A nice little improvement with this characteristic specific to the curvature of the circle.

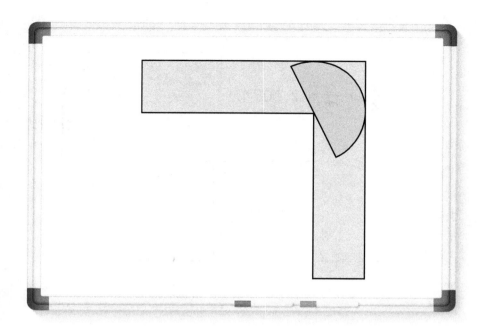

Here is where we can elicit our students' imagination, in considering how we could improve upon the semicircle model, while emphasizing that translation and rotation will be important considerations. My guess is that the collective curiosities of students, working within the relatively straightforward parameters of the problem, would come up with some creative sketches—maybe even verging on improving upon the area of 1.57.

The sofa problem was posed in 1966 by Leo Moser. Two years later, John Hammersley came up with a much-improved solution. As you can see, his sofa is made up of two quarter circles fused together with a rectangle, with a semicircle cutout (to aid in the rotation). Heck, it actually looks like a sofa one might have seen in the psychedelic '60s! Does it come in lime green? Along with the nifty design comes a nifty and memorable answer:

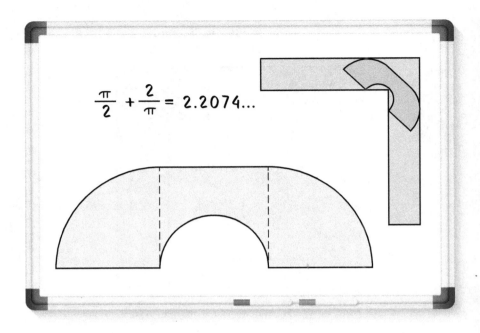

$$\frac{\pi}{2} + \frac{2}{\pi} = 2.2074\ldots$$

Twenty-six years later, an improvement was found by Joseph Gerver. It was *2.219 units²*. *A quarter of a century to improve the area by half of one percent.* This problem, like so many others, symbolizes the uncompromising zeal and passion mathematicians must have to want closure on the tiniest, trivial details of our world. And somewhere out there at least one mathematician is making it their life's work to find an even more optimal solution. Living for mathematics.

COMFORT

The sofa. Hmmmph. So comfortable. Have you ever talked about math while sitting on a sofa? I have only done it once, as far as I remember. San Antonio, 2017. I was there for the National Council of Supervisors of Mathematics Conference. I remember sitting on a couch in the conference center and talking to my friend Deborah Plowman Junk. It was just the two of us. We were each nestled into a corner of the sofa, and we spoke lazily and quixotically about what elementary mathematics should look like.

Too often, however, when we talk about math, we are standing in front of people, sitting at round tables, or moving from A to B. We are always comfortable talking about mathematics, but rarely are we *physically* comfortable during those discussions. Now, of course that is just the nature of where mathematics intersects with our lives—in the formality of education—but any ideas of wellness must incorporate, at least metaphorically, spaces and situations that support our physical comfort and our emotional comfort. Our desire for mathematics sociality and conviviality will spring from a desire to create *new emotions and experiences, a la Bourdain.*

Does mathematics currently have an invitation to a brunch date, an evening of beers on a patio, or a 2:00 a.m. campfire conversation with the sounds of a crackling fire and Neil Young washing over it? For the most part, no. And part of the problem is that we spend most of our time talking about *how to teach mathematics.* That is more shop talk. Nobody wants to talk shop in our leisure time. I repeat: *Nobody wants to talk shop in our leisure time.* And yet, the very book in your hands was leisurely written about one of the most popular leisure pursuits in the history of our planet.

When we discuss mathematics in a leisurely setting, we're much more likely to allow math to be what it really is: a translucent mess. One could easily imagine the following quote about mathematics from Bertrand Russell applying to any number of topics that might come up over a few pints (this timely quote was shared by Jo Boaler in 2020): "The subject in which we never know what we are talking about, or whether what we are saying is true."

Russell said this well after the birth of mathematics, but really before the birth of math education as we now know it. So, lamentably, that sentiment would be quite alien in our classrooms. For decades, thousands upon thousands of students have been asked to focus on the applications of mathematics, to engage in soul-crushing tests of performance, and to scramble for understanding in an unrealistic and unhealthy time frame—the epitome of a math to live mentality. Think of the huge range of emotions, topics, and activities you've experienced while hanging out in a comfortable living room with friends:

Truth, empathy, grace, humility, struggle, doubt, **beauty**, **meaning**, confusion, space, time, **play**, **exploration**, doodling, daydreaming, awe, wonder, magic, **permanence**, art, music, fantasy, power, weirdness, reverence, leisure, connection, **community, justice, freedom**, truth, humanity, hope, **flourishing**, and **love**.

The ones I have bolded are chapters in Francis Su's *Mathematics for Human Flourishing*. The others are all supportive and underexplored tributaries—meandering and washing over us in usually unexpected waves of wonder. Our mathematics should be shaped and colored by these attributes, and to foster rich memories of intellectual and *emotional* indulgence. For this simple reason: to want more. The mathematical health of our students will lie in this layered thirst. So, once again, we find the answer to math wellness nestled in the desirous and delirious verb of *chasing*.

We rarely talk about mathematics itself free from its curriculum constraints. The culprit is simply that we don't have time or aren't given the time. The consequence for this has always been an insidious accumulation of frustration that seems never enough to cause systemic change, but enough to cause mild fatigue and a vague sense of wrongdoing. Our pandemic became an unsurprising catalyst to reevaluate not just our own personal health and well-being, but that of math education. The sofa problem, for example, would not be found in the hallways of education's past. The answer as to why would be an embarrassing admission to the industrialization, mechanization, and homogeneity that drives math education—that we only *math to live*. We have to take far more risks in how/where/why we learn mathematics and strive to be emotionally and physically comfortable. That's what I would call "living to math."

But mathematics on its own—and it only existed for thousands of years before education threw it into the industrial meat grinder— is where we need to focus our solutions. Because the emphasis on applications and utility has been so engrained in our math education system, students always ask, "When will we use this?" But Su suggests the question should be: "When will I *value* this?" Moving from collective practicality to personal purpose, and reframing ourselves with the naked beauty of mathematics, liberated from the opacity of curriculum, is a pivot toward wellness.

That reframing really began on January 6, 2017. That was the date Francis Su gave this legendary speech as outgoing president of the Mathematical Association of America (MAA), when, if you recall from chapter four, he spoke about his friend Christopher, who is currently incarcerated on a thirty-two-year sentence for armed robbery in a federal prison:

> Right now, you've probably formed a mental image of who Christopher is, and you might be wondering why I'm opening my speech with his story. When you think about who does mathematics, both who is capable of doing mathematics and who wants to do mathematics, would you think of Christopher?
>
> And yet he wrote me a letter after seven years in prison. He said: "I've always had a proclivity for mathematics, but being in a very early stage of youth and also living in some adverse circumstances, I never came to understand the true meaning and benefit of pursuing an education . . . over the last three years, I have purchased and studied a multitude of books to give me a profound and concrete understanding of Algebra I, Algebra II, college algebra, geometry, trigonometry, Calculus I, and Calculus II." Christopher was writing me for help in furthering his mathematics education.
>
> When you think of who does mathematics, do you think of Christopher?
>
> "Every being cries out silently to be read differently."

If you were in attendance that night, you probably did not cry out silently, to paraphrase the Simone Weil quote at the end of Su's speech. In fact, many people came up to him that night in tears. The good life with mathematics should be available to all—as it always has. Regrettably, our society has made mathematics an elitist, competitive sport. If you are not going to use it to pursue a career, then its value falls off appreciably. This is the poisonous myth that has been part of our math education system for decades. However, on that January night, a quiet watershed moment occurred for all to witness, or hear about later.

HOPELESS ROMANTICISM

Peter Taylor referenced the Romantic period of student learning. Francis Su has spoken endlessly about flourishing and the good life with mathematics. Both ideas collided in 2013 in a most unexpected place—an ice fishing shack. It was in an episode from the first season of *Parts Unknown*, where Anthony Bourdain visits Quebec, probably motivated by Montreal being his favorite Canadian city. As a lifetime Torontonian, I can wholeheartedly agree with this sentiment.

In the opening of the episode, Bourdain is ice fishing on the Saint Lawrence River, then having lunch with restaurateurs Fred Morin and David McMillan inside a dilapidated blue shack with dimensions better suited to describing bathrooms or walk-in closets. Even so, there was warmth and comfort, and it seemed there was nowhere else in the world any of them would have wanted to be at that moment. The conversation centered around food as an unheralded joy of life. Specifically, as pertains to this chapter, they were discussing the philosophy of *living to eat*. As Morin and McMillan wax poetic about nostalgic French dishes and vintage cutlery, Bourdain calls them "hopeless romantics."

The *art of living* is the larger arc under discussion by all those huddled in this tiny hut, with a wood stove used for both heating and cooking. To enjoy every detail of a meal and share it with unbridled vigor with those around you. To let the chemistry of the company and alchemy of ingredients create the most organic output of such experiences—gratitude. Our math classrooms have the potential for this *eudaimonia*—prosperity, welfare, and blessedness. Choose rich problems and investigations, perhaps one with a quirky story, hook, or surprise—much like the "24" problem that opened this book. (Yes, I still owe you the delicious proof—I haven't forgotten!)

Treat mathematics with the same reverence all cultures give their food and specialty dishes. There is no path to wellness that can be reached if we continue to see mathematics only through a practical and competitive lens—and especially if these aspects are oversold and overvalued, blandly packaged to arrive quickly and serviceably. *Mathematics should be about walking to Mecca, not taking an Uber to the mall.*

While I was never a good salesperson for math education—falsely hawking its wares like factoring and trigonometry as essential ideas in the outside world—I also don't remember ever talking about mathematics in this soulful manner before I started writing books. But there were no shortcuts to get to this point. I needed twenty years of classroom efficiency married with life's pleasures, challenges, and heartaches to get there—to see mathematics as an emotional experience and journey.

Besides Peter Harrison and a few others, the math world reflected at me for my entire teaching career gave me little space, motivation, or affirmation to nurture a voice of *Bourdainian romanticism* for mathematics. So while my teaching career was filled with amazing connections with students, most of it was made through a dutiful responsibility to a math curriculum I wasn't in love with.

Sure, I got paid handsomely for being a math teacher. But it also broke me. That's why near the end of my teaching career the only thing I held onto tightly was the idea that the best things we do as teachers are immeasurable. However, even that belief had an expiration date. I had nothing left to give. What I could give as a teacher was outpaced by what was taken out of me. It pained me to dole out curriculum as sterile code—7.1 on Monday, 7.2 on Tuesday, quiz on Wednesday, 7.3 on Thursday, announce test on Friday. Lather. Rinse. Repeat. Quitting became the only option.

In October of 2017, Canada's largest newspaper, the *Globe and Mail*, published my op-ed piece about my reasons for leaving the classroom. I probably wouldn't have had the motivation to write it if not for a clichéd outpouring of disappointment over Ontario's low standardized test scores. Has anyone ever just imagined what our world would look like if every student got perfect scores on these tests? Would our society benefit? Would there be more gratitude, kindness, and compassion in the world? Standardized tests are the two-dollar DVDs you sometimes see near the checkout aisle of grocery stores. That is exactly their value for most math teachers. The actual letter was longer but was edited for space. This is how it appeared in the newspaper:

> As a math teacher, there were many days I hated math more than my students did. Way more.
>
> So I quit in 2013, happily leaving behind job security, a pension and the holy grail of teacher benefits: summers off.
>
> Everyone thought I was crazy. I was in the early years of a divorce and had a mother and two kids to support. Almost nobody—and rightfully so, I suppose—supported my ostensibly hasty decision to abandon the education ship. There were no safety boats waiting and I was not a great swimmer. What the hell was I thinking?
>
> In fact I was leaping off the *Titanic*—where actual math education is relegated to third class and was drowning along with its students.
>
> The hardest thing to teach is mathematics. Not so much because math is hard—so is shooting three-pointers or making risotto—but because education makes it hard. Boring curriculum. Constant testing. Constant arguments over pedagogy. Lack of time. It's a *Gong Show*.

I found a sizable chunk of the math that I was forced to teach either a) boring; b) benign; c) banal; or d) Byzantine. The guilt of being paid to shovel this anachronistic heap of emaciated and disconnected mathematics around finally caught up with me.

I quit because I felt like a charlatan when I implicitly or explicitly told my students that what we were learning reflected the heart of mathematics or that it was the core of lifelong practicality. "When are we going to use this?" has been the No. 1 whine in math classes for a few generations. We should stop trying to sell mathematics for its usefulness. It's not why you or I should learn it.

Earlier this year, Francis Su, the outgoing president of the Mathematical Association of America, gave a speech for the ages. He referenced a prisoner named Christopher serving a long prison sentence, teaching himself mathematics. "Mathematics helps people flourish," he said. "Mathematics is for human flourishing." In a follow-up interview, Su talked about how math should involve beauty, truth, justice, love and play. Not sure about you, but my math education and Ontario teaching experience were the furthest things from these virtues. In Ontario, kids are imprisoned with criminally bland mathematics—so are the teachers.

I left teaching because my impact on math education lay beyond my classroom and my school. I felt I could contribute my passion/understanding for mathematics on a larger stage—maybe global. I was dreaming, but sometimes chasing your dreams is worth all the outside skepticism and uphill climbs. At one point, I was penniless at 50, stressed, confused and disappointed. But I wasn't unhappy. I was rescued by the light and humanity of mathematics.

Fast forward four years. I've written a book about the hidden happiness of math. I work remotely for a Canadian digital math resource company and I travel all over North America speaking about my almost gnawing passion of mathematics. I felt that I couldn't share that passion for most of my teaching career because the unchecked bureaucracy of the education system was more interested in data from standardized test scores and putting pedagogy ahead of mathematics. As such, the culture of mathematics has almost been shaded into obscurity.

So now, when I see the flood of math articles about Ontario's low math scores, I put my head in my hands and worry my eyes might just roll too far back into my head.

Every year is a contest to see who will win this year's huffing and puffing award about the province's low standardized test scores. For the past few years, arguments about old math versus new math have been running away with the trophy. Although, headlines crying Elementary Teachers Need More Math Training are often the runner-up.

As a student, I went through that "old" system. Sure, I got plenty of As and gold stars, but it took me well into my teaching career to really understand a fraction of the things I thought I knew.

Calculus? Pfff. Get rid of that thing, it belongs in university after a serious boot camp of algebra. Fractions, as with unsafe firecrackers, need to be pulled out of the hands of younger students and introduced to them in their hormonal years. Why are teachers asking students to flip and multiply fractions when you need to divide them? Anyone care to explain that to children—why fractions are doing gymnastics to arrive at the correct answer?

There are so many amazing teachers fighting the good fight. But until the real culprit—the government—gets called out for manufacturing a dog's breakfast of math education, students will continue to suffer in the classroom.

"Suffering" isn't being dramatic. If anything, I undersold the harmful potential of learning mathematics in an environment of immense pressure and detachment. Many of you are probably familiar with Vicki Abeles's films *Race to Nowhere* and *Beyond Measure*. Here is the letter she wrote to viewers about her first project, back in 2009:

Dear Friends,

Several years ago, my only knowledge of film came from buying tickets at the box office and going to see a movie with my kids. But I was inspired to make Race to Nowhere after a series of wake-up calls made me look closely at our education system—and at the relentless pressure it puts on our children and families.

Like many parents, I witnessed strain and fatigue in my own children as they navigated days filled with school, homework, tutoring, and extracurricular activities. Then, after months of watching our 12-year-old daughter spend long evenings battling homework assignments, studying for tests, and suffering panic attacks in the middle of the night, my husband and I found her doubled over in pain, and we rushed her to the emergency room. Her cheerful façade and determination to keep up had hidden her symptoms from us, her friends, and her teachers. When she was diagnosed with a stress-induced illness, I was determined to do something.

I started to make some changes in my home, but many of the pressures on my children and family felt systemic and beyond my control. I felt the need to raise awareness about the unhealthy and out-of-balance educational culture we were experiencing, and to bring communities together to galvanize change at a large scale. Films had always been a powerful force in my life, so I decided to capture the stories of my children, their peers, and those on the frontlines of education—teachers and students—on camera. Race to Nowhere was born.

After interviewing students, parents and teachers, I met with top education and child development experts at Stanford University and other leading institutions. I interviewed my own daughter and went on camera myself to lend personal context to the national story I could see emerging. Several months into the film's development, without any warning signs, a 13-year-old girl in our community committed suicide after getting a poor grade on a math test. This local tragedy added yet more urgency to the need for change.

Now, more than two years after the film's premiere, I am joined by millions of educators, parents, policymakers, and students who see that childhood has become indentured to test scores, performance, and competition. Together, we are facing an epidemic of unhealthy, disengaged, unprepared kids trying to manage as best they can. We agree that we cannot keep silent any longer, and that we cannot wait for government or large institutions to make the radical changes our kids need today. We agree that layers of change are needed, starting from the ground up.

It is my hope that Race to Nowhere creates a jumping-off point for that grassroots change—a forum where we can join forces to transform education and reclaim healthy childhood one community at a time. Thank you for watching, for bringing the Race to Nowhere conversation to your own community, and for acting on what you see.

Sincerely,
Vicki H. Abeles

While there is a lot of disheartening information here that explains Vicki Abeles's almost fated journey from Wall Street lawyer to film-maker, there is one sentence that cannot be unseen. You know which one. And, having a daughter who is currently twelve, I have to, as a writer, as a math educator, and as a father, try my hardest to *imagine it*. I have to imagine the spiraling weight of anxiety and depression on my own daughter not performing well in math. I have to imagine her thinking that not living is a better choice than suffering with math. I have to imagine the light leaving her eyes.

That was one of the hardest things I have ever written. But, it was necessary. The girl who took her own life probably had many things in common with my own daughter. I needed to feel that tragedy with as much stabbing pain as I could, and be extra vigilant in writing about mathematical wellness as a bloody moral imperative for our children. No less than our very lives and the lives of our loved ones hang in the balance.

GATEKEEPER

It's been a while. Seven years in the making. But Vicki Abeles's next documentary, *The Gatekeeper: Math in America*, will be finished in 2021. I was honored to be interviewed for this film, which squarely looks at the toll toxic learning environments have played in the health issues of our students and the race/class bias in math classrooms all over the United States.

Coincidentally—or not—in 2021 the Gates Foundation will announce the winners of its first challenge related to US education, as well. Specifically, in mathematics. Well, it's actually more specific than that. It's about reimagining the gatekeeper course: Algebra 1. It definitely feels like the revolutionary planets of math education are deciding to line up in kicking off the first year of this new decade.

As well, we must cast a wider net when looking at what gatekeeping has done in mathematics. It can't just be seen as blocking success and career options. Those are important. But, instead of fixing this gate that leads to a clichéd, well-worn path of usefulness and practicality, how about we just shepherd students to a broader road that highlights math as simply a beautiful part of our lives?

One of the things I knew when I started writing this book was that Anthony Bourdain's life and travels would come to symbolize a chapter of this book. I have read all his books. I have watched every episode of *A Cook's Tour, No Reservations, The Layover, Raw Craft,* and *Parts Unknown.* His many, many musings, subtle and in symphony with the moment, carry life lessons. And, naturally, some of them can be extracted for math lessons. It is no surprise, then, that a riveting and emotional documentary of his fascinating life, *Roadrunner: A Film About Anthony Bourdain,* came out in the summer of 2021. Like many others, it took me a while to come to terms with his death. As ardent admirers of his complex personality of candor, curiosity, and kindness, the documentary only confirmed the pain that his death brought us. And, as is too often the case, the value of his presence to the world was only truly felt in the permanence of his absence. His wisdom has been warmly, effortlessly, and constantly suffused in my relationship with mathematics. If you have watched his shows, you have seen him look out at some life-altering vistas in stunned silence and admiration. The landscape of mathematics offers the same affirmative contemplation of a quiet "wow." Wanderlust can exist in mathematics. Treat it like the adventure it is, and you will find it!

When Bourdain visits a friend's restaurant in New York and is surprised at red wine being served with sea bass, he waxes poetic about how we need to be surprised more by what is put in front of us. Mathematics is the story of surprises. Yet we always seem to be pairing *a white wine with fish.* We are hustling math as procedural and routine. We are nowhere near the edges of math that we can take our students to. In an early *A Cook's Tour* episode, Bourdain is in the middle of the Sahara—his first major encounter with one of those life-changing landscapes—and dusk is setting in. He is lying in the reddish sand, reflecting on how a "loser" like himself could be sitting there, experiencing this once-in-a-lifetime moment. He then says, "Life finally lives up to its advertising." When does math live up to its advertising? How do we put every student on a sloping desert hill in the middle of nowhere so they can have a similar epiphany? Math is beautiful. Selling it as anything else is selling it tragically short.

THE MAGIC LABYRINTH

Despite my vast interest in other universes and new ideas and space, travel and time travel, which by the way I think is impossible, the basic thing is human character, which is the main thing of most writers.
—Philip José Farmer

The inspiration for the title of this chapter comes from *The Magic Labyrinth*, the fourth book in the celebrated Riverworld series by sci-fi writer Philip José Farmer. That title itself comes from the 1880 poem *The Kasidah of Haji Abdu El-Yezdi*. It's a poem that Sir Richard Burton, the British explorer and Arabist—and main character in Riverworld—wrote under a pseudonym. The poem is almost a thousand lines long, broken into quatrains. It is a wild and mystical ride of a read that was written to bring Sufi wisdom to the West. While there are many verses from Burton's poem that could sit comfortably within this book, I plucked out this one: "To seek the True, to glad the heart, such is of life the Higher Law."

Seek. Chasing. *Glad the heart*. Wellness. *Higher Law*. Mathematics. These are words that will hopefully resonate with all of you. For me, when I first came across that verse, I was in utter disbelief that the title of my book, at least in spirit, was carved out over a hundred years ago, modestly placed in a lengthy poem of historical significance. While I wrote this book with a *future* repurposing of mathematics in mind, that future can only arrive by giving space, time, and light to its colorful *past*. The humble cobbling together of the mathematical ideas, problems, and stories so far have really been to speak to mathematics' own magic labyrinth—its history.

Remember partitions from chapter five? If you noticed, I told partitions as a story. Characters were introduced. The narrative slowly developed to attract interest. Suspenseful buildup. Dramatic plot twist. Conclusion. Mathematics is a collection of stories, not just bullet points of facts. Stories imply humanization. Facts siphon it out. That is what often separates stories from history. History can be told without stories. Teaching mathematics without its stories is emotionally empty. There are thousands upon thousands of them. Too many of them. All filled with human characters. That is the lifeblood of all stories—even those mathematical in nature.

And frankly, this chapter is by no means an attempt to distill the many beautiful *books* on the history of mathematics into *pages*. The goal here is to simply lure you into the labyrinth. Also, my guide duties will be purposefully brief. This will be your journey. This will be your story. The unfolding will constantly be a mystery. Every turn in this enormous labyrinth will contribute to a unique journey of exploration and discovery. None of us will have the same adventures as we skip and scamper through the stories, myths, and fables that color the terrain of mathematics.

You notice I didn't use the word "facts." That was intentional. Facts, to me, are information that has been removed from a much more organic narrative, rendering it almost lifeless—a calculated sapping of the color from the meandering lives of humans. We cannot be connected by facts alone, which metaphorically probably get housed in our brain as beige index cards in gray file cabinets in a white room. Facts might connect the dots, but stories color them and bend the lines between them. Stories provide dimension and tentacles of emotion that connect to other stories. How the color of stories shapes our lives is unpredictable. How the initial splatter bores deep down inside of us and entangles kindly with our constantly unfurling of life's path is a cherished mystery. We don't just reside in these colors, we live for these colors. Even more, we live to *share these colors*.

Stories are more than transmitters of information. Stories are transmitters of energy. Remember when Conway broke down in front of an audience while telling a story about the first International Math Congress? That story must have resided within him for decades, entangling with other memories and visions of mathematics. Even though the story brought him to tears, he could *not* have anticipated that. The moment caught him as equally off guard as it did the audience.

> I would love to live like a river flow, carried by the surprise of its own unfolding.
> —Jack Donahue

The best chance we give ourselves to invite emotions as permanent guests into our world of mathematics *is to be a permanent guest in the history of mathematics* and live our learning with one surprising delight after another. Who knows? Maybe we will have an unsuspecting moment where our own memories will become perceptible markers of our love affair with mathematical stories. It might not be as dramatic as uncontrollable tears, but maybe a heavy sigh or a coded smirk to let those around you know a little bit about the impact of mathematics on your life.

WHY WE LOVE STORIES

Oxytocin. The "feel-good" hormone. This is what gets released when we bear witness to a great story unfold. Facts, on the other hand, trigger the data-processing parts of our brain. Stories hit our sensory parts.

They make us feel connected to something bigger, awash in memorable feelings of empathy and trust. While the whole Pixar film *Up* is memorable, the first five minutes leave an emotional tattoo on anyone who has seen it. The story of Ellie and Carl meeting as kids, falling in love, and growing old together is captured with perfect lightness and buoyancy, matching the title of the film. Seeing Ellie get sick and die is the deflating finale to that opening sequence that leaves so many, including me, in a puddle of tears. But nobody should be surprised by the emotional investment we give to stories.

But can mathematics history really give us similar experiences of emotional investment? Well, the answer to that question lies in another question: Do we want all our students to have a deep understanding of mathematics—content, purpose, and value? If stories are the best way to connect and a deep understanding of math is the goal of every teacher, then the bridge to connect the two is *not too far*.

To be frank, without stories—and the associated absence of integrated humanness—there is no hope. All that would be left is an abyss of dried-up ideas. Thankfully, an oasis of our own humanity has been left for us to slowly cobble together something honoring the emotional depth of mathematics.

One of the benefits of being a part of Generation X is laying claim to having grown up as a kid in the greatest period of Saturday morning cartoons—the '70s. It was not only breakfast we devoured growing up, but we also had an insatiable appetite for everything animated. For many of us, our first introduction to rich and compelling history came in the early '70s with *The Wonderful Stories of Professor Kitzel*. The producers of the show were clever enough to give us bite-sized morsels of historical events, around five minutes—long enough to devour a bowl of cereal.

The format of each episode was generally an introductory discussion of the subject by the professor. He would then take the viewer to his time machine, pull a lever, and the story would begin. Halfway through, the professor would interrupt to make some humorous remark before returning to the narrative with the invitation: "Let's see what happened next." Each episode then concluded with some humorous closing sequence. The animation was nothing to write home about. But there was something inexplicable that happened when the professor would saunter over to the time machine. A sense of anticipation eclipsed the subpar visuals.

The story of the Oracle of Delphi captured my imagination. The Oracle was the center of the Greek empire, and to learn that only women held the position of the seer, the *Pythia*, was something I found fascinating. In later years, I would revisit this story and learn much more about this spiritual place and where it sat in Greek lore. What is the result of hearing a great story from history? You want to hear another one. That is it. I simply wanted to hear *another story*. Nobody in the history of the earth has ever been satiated with stories to the point where they might say, "I'm good." We are wired to love stories, and we are wired to want more of them.

While stories vary with every generation and culture, many share these common hallmarks:

- Conflict
- Tension
- Surprise
- Extraordinary characters
- Controversy
- Mystery
- Suspense

Even the simple story of the wild pig and the sea cow contained many of these elements: conflict, tension, surprise, and extraordinary characters. In my keynotes, which usually last an hour, that story takes about half a minute. Yet so much is communicated in lessons and morals that can benefit our shared humanity. It's why you will never forget this wonderful story. All these markers of rich and compelling narrative are scattered throughout the history of mathematics, permeating every race, culture, and civilization that has inhabited this planet. *The Crest of the Peacock: Non-European Roots of Mathematics* by George Gheverghese Joseph is a Herculean effort to not just share these over-looked roots of mathematics, but to show their trajectory in the overall development of the field. The mathematics is delightfully dense. In the third printing of the book, the following opening paragraph was added, speaking to the general importance of history and making a convincing case for its being central to understanding ourselves and the world around us:

> An interest in history marks us for life. How we see our-selves and others is shaped by the history we absorb, not only in the classroom but also from the Internet, films, newspapers, television programs, novels, even strip car-toons. From the time we first become aware of the past, it can fire our imagination and excite our curiosity.

The history of mathematics lies patiently in wait to ignite the imagination and curiosities of a new generation of students and teach-ers. So, how do we do it? By luring them into the lair of its lore. Here are five stories from the labyrinth that I want to share with you. Each one I believe, on its own, can cast a spell of boundless curiosity for us to step inside. I have tried my best to write these stories as I would *tell* these stories.

A STORY OF WISDOM

I know what you're thinking. Isn't every story, regardless of it being math-related, drizzled in universal wisdom? Absolutely! So why then did I go with such an unimaginative title? Because this story of mathe-matics involves an actual place—a library, in ninth-century Baghdad—that was called the House of Wisdom. While we know for sure that it no longer exists and even the traces of its earlier existence are faint, at least three books have been written about the mystery and intrigue of this library. I love this little passage that I found from a children's book about it:

> Young Ishaq wanders through 9th-century Baghdad's packed marketplace, filled with curiosity, awed by the many different people and languages. "They speak so strangely," he whispers to his father. His father, a translator and scribe who works in the caliph's library, the House of Wisdom, replies sagely, "You may not understand them, but that does not mean they have nothing to say."

Now let's add the fact that this mythical place became a birthplace for modern mathematics. Are we not hooked now?

The story goes that the House of Wisdom became a kind of intellectual center of the world, bringing in people of all backgrounds and faiths to study mathematics and every other subject imaginable: astronomy, medicine, chemistry, geography, philosophy, literature, and the arts, and even more suspicious subjects, such as alchemy and astrology. Kind of like a Hogwarts without wands and wizardry! The House of Wisdom was a major landmark in the thematic development of mathematics.

Unfortunately, the House of Wisdom was destroyed in the middle of the twelfth century by the invading Mongols. Legend has it that so many transcripts were thrown in the Tigris River that the water turned black from the ink. While none of this can be verified, the mathematics developed around this time by Arab mathematicians is one of the shining moments in the history of mathematics, specifically algebra. The most famous of them was al-Khwarizmi, who not only gave us the word *algebra*—*al-jabr* (Arabic for "removal of subtracted terms")— but whose name, when latinized, is where the word *algorithm* comes from. Safe to say that the title "Father of Algebra" is usually associated with al-Khwarizmi.

However, inasmuch as the House of Wisdom was a hotbed for researching and translating all the rich mathematics from India, it also valued the dissemination and propagation of this knowledge to the public. Stanford University mathematician Keith Devlin is one of the best people around to tell the birth of algebra around this time. In fact, he enthusiastically advocates that Baghdad of this era was equivalent to Silicon Valley during the '80s and '90s, and the exponential explosion of technology used by the public during that time. These feverish confluences of academia and the desire for mass consumption were found a millennium apart. Great things come in cycles—long cycles!

So, I guess there had to be a "Steve Jobs" somewhere in this story, right? And the answer is yes. We met him earlier in the book: Leonardo of Pisa, someone who came into the picture several hundred years later. Maybe you know him from such famous sequences as the Fibonacci sequence—even though it was first discovered a hundred years earlier by an Indian poet, Hemachandra, who fleshed out the numbers 2, 3, 5, 8, 13, 21, 34, etc. by examining Sanskrit poetry and the use of short and long vowels. As you can see, mathematics is a tapestry. It's challenging trying to stay within just a colorful patch or two.

While Leonardo of Pisa's groundbreaking book, *Liber Abaci*, didn't come out until 1202, when he was in his thirties, the seeds of the book had been fortuitously planted when he was a teenager, when he joined his father in the North African port of Bugia. His father had moved there from Pisa for business interests with the Arabic-speaking world. The port became a literal portal for a young boy to marvel at the wisdom of Arabic mathematics that had migrated there through the Silk Road, and to have the "Apple-ish" foresight to later bring these innovative and methodical calculation techniques to not just Italy, but eventually the whole of Europe, leading to a commercial and financial revolution around the fourteenth century. None of the original 1202 copies remain and only three copies of the second edition exist in adequate condition, all of which are in Italy. The whole riveting story can be found in Keith Devlin's book *The Man of Numbers: Fibonacci's Arithmetic Revolution*.

The characters in this story are memorable. Leonardo of Pisa for his age. Hemachandra for being the first person to discover the "rabbit" numbers we have historically attributed to Fibonacci (a name that was given to him much later). They are also surprising. There is conflict as to what the true origin of the famous sequence is. Tension is developed in knowing that the House of Wisdom no longer exists. There is much more to know. Google away!

A STORY OF LOST KNOWLEDGE

This story is about zero. To be specific, the *untold* story of zero. Well, geez, technically, that is not entirely true. The story was once told in its entirety by the Indian mathematicians and astronomers Aryabhata, Bhāskara, and Brahmagupta over a thousand years ago. Yes, the story was initially communicated through spoken poetry (remember writing materials like papyrus and bark would have been hard to come by). In my first book, the first chapter was dedicated to zero. However, while I detailed some of its colorful origins and mysticism, I was rather ignorant of its strange migration to the West through Islamic scholars. Remember the game Broken Telephone? This zero story is the almost fourteen-hundred-year-old version of that game—and it is still going! Just look at your typical QWERTY keyboard.

Do you see where zero is? Right at the very end, almost like an afterthought. While we may not begin our counting with zero—though we should—having it come after nine seems to symbolize the lack of understanding of what role zero is supposed to play in arithmetic. It was meant to be the central character in not only the laws of arithmetic, but in the laws of the universe! Instead, it became an understudy, a minor character, in one ridiculously confusing play of mathematics. Let's start at the beginning. But before we do that, let's reveal our storyteller: Jonathan Crabtree. When we tell stories to our friends, they often interlace with other stories or have a tendency to meander. With Crabtree, it is both!

Jonathan Crabtree is an Australian historian who has spent more than thirty years trying to recover the lost treasure of Indian mathematics—zero. It would not be a stretch to call him the Indiana Jones of ancient mathematics archivists. In fact, his own website (jonathan-crabtree.com) makes it clear that this is the essence of his mission in life. But how did a person who earned an economics degree end up consumed by the rich history of Indian mathematics? Well, it has to do with a pivotal event in 1983, when Crabtree broke his back, and it was uncertain if he would ever walk again. His recovery soon became an inspiration. And, in 1987, a newspaper in Australia did a story on him. In the article he was quoted: "I hope to change the way the Western World teaches mathematics."

That goal has not changed, which is why I am sharing this story. Crabtree's passion to unravel the mystery of zero's deeper significance—and its tragic omission from the general history of mathematics—is a burning light that should attract us all. Crabtree has weathered some significant losses in life—including the death of a child. It would have been understandable if the sum of these setbacks derailed him. In fact, it has been quite the opposite. Perhaps because the search and rescue of zero's lost history is a humanitarian mission. So let's travel back to seventh-century India and begin to unpack the story that Crabtree has been writing for more than three decades.

Zero was supposed to be the lowest number. That's it. Nothing was supposed to go below zero. How is walking seven feet to the left less than walking three feet to the right? How is it less than walking one foot to the right? Is the charge on an electron (-1) somehow less than the charge on a positron ($+1$)? Of course not. But these real-life situations are part of the problem of confusing students and teachers about the arithmetic that revolves around zero in terms of positive numbers and their opposite or negative numbers. I know. We are so ingrained with the traditional number line and looking at positive and negative numbers through the lens we grew up with that it is challenging to adopt a new model. Except this model is hardly new. It is incredibly old. It's the original one. It is the one that would make the most sense to younger children if this is what they saw first. Let us try to look at it through that perspective.

Do you really, really think that children were supposed to learn a problem like 1 − 2 *five years after* learning 2 − 1? The unwarranted separation of positive and negative numbers is the most glaring symptom that we merely mapped our historical misunderstanding of zero and negative numbers onto our math education, then called it a day.

In 628 CE, Brahmagupta wrote his main work, *Brāhmasphutasiddhānta*. While a good chunk of it was astronomical in nature—and that is important—there were many key mathematical ideas, including the critical work surrounding zero. Here are Brahmagupta's 18 Sutras of Symmetry, as summarized by Crabtree. While many of these laws of addition, subtraction, multiplication, and division might seem like common sense, our final misunderstanding on the meaning of zero in mathematics, physics, and astronomy shows that we didn't do a great job extracting all that common sense contained within them:

- The sum of two positive quantities is positive.
- The sum of two negative quantities is negative.
- The sum of zero and a negative number is negative.
- The sum of zero and a positive number is positive.
- The sum of zero and zero is zero.
- The sum of a positive and a negative is their difference; or, if they are equal, zero.
- In subtraction, the less is to be taken from the greater, positive from positive.
- In subtraction, the less is to be taken from the greater, negative from negative.
- When the greater, however, is subtracted from the less, the difference is reversed.
- When positive is to be subtracted from negative, and negative from positive, they must be added together.

- The product of a negative quantity and a positive quantity is negative.
- The product of two negative quantities is positive.
- The product of two positive quantities is positive.
- Positive divided by positive or negative by negative is positive.
- Positive divided by negative is negative. Negative divided by positive is negative.
- Zero divided by a negative or positive number is either zero or is expressed as a fraction with zero as numerator and the finite quantity as denominator.
- A positive or negative number when divided by zero is a fraction with zero as denominator.*
- Zero divided by zero is zero.*

These laws don't align with modern mathematics, but they were the first attempt to define division by zero.

A wonderful visual Crabtree created was to *bend* the number line at zero, so that it becomes literally the lowest point on a number line. The definition of zero that Brahmagupta intended is clear in the picture below—the *sum* of a positive and negative number of equal magnitudes is equal to zero. There is also a similar diagram to the correct interpretation of positive and negative values by the Chinese (the first appearance of zero in a Chinese text was in 1247 BCE).

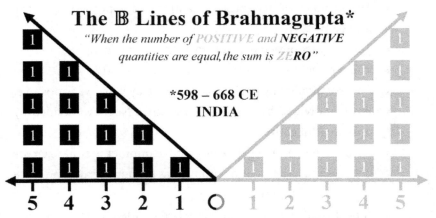

Jonathan J. Crabtree | jonathancrabtree.com | podometic.in

We already do zero pairs in our classrooms, but we don't truly unleash that power to help students with questions involving negatives. In the question below, the quick standard is to instruct students to make the two minus signs a positive so that the question is now 2 + 5. While this achieves the correct answer, that is all that is achieved. There is no discussion as to the confusion that surely must lie in this situation. That confusion takes on a little clarity if we treat negatives and positives as objects. So now, it should be clear that it is currently impossible to do this question—we have 2 of one kind of object trying to subtract 5 of a different kind of object.

Adding zero as the next step might trigger a variety of responses, but the overwhelming one should be that adding zero does not change the question! And, finally, in the second to last line, we have *five negatives take away five negatives*. Same number of objects subtract same number of objects is always zero.

$$2 - (-5)$$

Two positives take away five negatives

Add zero → $2 + 0 - (-5)$

Add a "specific" zero → $2 + (-5+5) - (-5)$

$$7 + (-5) - (-5)$$

$$7 + 0$$

Let's look at this question again—without the abstraction of the Hindu-Arabic numerals.

> Let □ = $^+1$ and ■ = $^-1$
> Two positives take away five negatives becomes
> □□ take away ■ ■ ■ ■ ■, which can't be done! So we
> use Brahmagupta's Addition Sutra #5 and add a zero in
> the form of five positives and five negatives. Now we have
> □□ and □□□□□■ ■ ■ ■ ■ take away ■ ■ ■ ■ ■,
> which can be done, giving □□ and □□□□□ or seven
> positives. $^+2 - {^-5} = {^+7}$.

So? What went wrong? What went squirrely? How did the mathematical world not take a *left at Albuquerque*? Crabtree's theory has to do with what the Arab mathematicians like al-Khwarizmi did with the twenty-four-chapter *Brāhmasphutasiddhānta*. Since much of the arithmetic and algebra works by these scholars were rooted in practical applications of inheritance and trading, it could be likely that the chapter on zero—more rooted in laws of the universe—was ignored.

And since Brahmagupta's work on arithmetic, traveling along the Silk Road, would only make it to Western mathematicians via the Middle East, only what was heavily emphasized was going to be known. Zero's fate of being relegated to a placeholder was sealed by that drop of the mathematical baton.

So that is what Jonathan Crabtree has been doing for most of his life. Trying to find that baton and pass it off to the world—as it should have been over a thousand years ago. The best part of this story is that it is not over! I urge you to follow him at @jcrabtree on Twitter and spend many hours on his scholarly research that can be found on his website, podometic.in. He should be launching his children's books on *podometic* (a term he came up with to imply a new and improved arithmetic system) sometime in 2021. What better way to start the whole story of zero than with young children?

A STORY OF COURAGE

Sometimes we forget that math history takes place in general history, and we probably don't think of the thematic development of mathematics intersecting with the general events of global history. Well, we should. What if a young Leonardo of Pisa hadn't followed his father to Bugia? What if Amy Alznauer's father hadn't found Ramanujan's lost notes in 1976? What if Western mathematicians didn't display cultural bias toward Brahmagupta's law of zero? All these "what if" questions are rooted in human experiences and possibilities, which invariably affect history on some scale. Sometimes they are minor, and sometimes they affect the trajectory of events in major ways. Math history involves the actions/nonactions of general human concerns—things we might all come across in life-changing moments. I would not have written this book if I hadn't lost my first high school teaching job and met my mathematical guide/sorcerer, Peter Harrison. Its evolution was a consequence of those events. One of the most powerful stories about life events influencing math events involves a teenage girl in the time of the French Revolution. Her name was Sophie Germain.

Many of you probably already know the story. But this is *my* story of Sophie Germain. What I mean by this is *how* I love to tell the story, with points that resonate with me. The "my" is not about possession, it is about love. I would love to listen to someone else's version! And if it wasn't for the Bastille having fallen in the summer of 1789, the flashpoint of the French Revolution, maybe the proof of Fermat's enigma would not have happened in 1993. Sure, that is speculative. But I believe there is some truth in my provocation! Maybe I should tell the story to see if there is any merit to my storytelling bait . . .

So yes, the streets had become unsafe with the toppling of this political prison, as the revolution against the French monarchists was now fully ignited. As such, people, especially children, were discouraged to be on the streets. One of those children was thirteen-year-old Sophie Germain, who was now confined to her apartment. Naturally bored, she began wandering around her father's library, which by all accounts was not a place Sophie was typically allowed. At some point—actually more of an inflection—she came across a book that contained the supposed story of Archimedes's death. As the story goes, Archimedes was concentrating on a geometric problem involving circles when a Roman soldier attacked and killed him. According to William Rankin, author of *Introducing Newton: A Graphic Guide*, these were Archimedes's last words: "Noli turbare circulos meos!"

Without even knowing any Latin, those last words seem dramatic enough for a Shakespeare play! (By the way, did you know that the only play Shakespeare wrote that contains the word *mathematics* is *The Taming of the Shrew*?) Translated, those words mean "Do not disturb my circles." Now, we don't know if Sophie saw those words in the book she read, but she consumed the story they were a part of. Imagine a thirteen-year-old girl who, just months earlier might have been playing outside in the Paris streets, unencumbered by the details of mathematics and its history, coming across this story.

Sophie's world was pretty much shaken up like a snow globe upon coming across this story. She was now under the spell of mathematics. Her appetite for it was so large that she also taught herself Latin and Greek, the predominant languages of the math books in her father's library. But while Sophie was excited to embark on this new, mysterious journey, her father was not too keen. So a cat and mouse game began with lamps and blankets—items Sophie needed to study math at night. Her parents would take away these essential things for the cold and dark nights that were to come, but Sophie would replace them with candles and garments.

Can you imagine a teenage girl teaching herself mathematics with merely the modest light of a flickering candle? The French Revolution is happening outside, and inside, Sophie Germain is teaching herself differential calculus. Why hasn't there been a movie about this yet? But that story, gripping unto itself, is only the beginning of several twists and turns in the mathematical life of Sophie Germain.

Her parents finally relented and stopped discouraging her from pursuing her interest in mathematics. By the age of eighteen, Sophie had taught herself math all the way up to basic calculus. Her determination, resilience, and passion in learning mathematics in less than supportive environments were a barometer for her accomplishments still to come. But the road ahead was going to be anything but straightforward. While a new school, École Polytechnique, opened in 1794 to train mathematicians and scientists, women were forbidden to study there. And though women of the aristocrat class had access to such education, Sophie, being from a middle-class family, had no such opportunities. Fortunately, she had the drive of mathematical intuition and curiosity to fuel her battles with the social norms and prejudices of the time. Nothing was going to hold her back.

She managed to obtain lecture notes from the school and study from them—independent study defined her teenage years. One of the prominent mathematicians at the school was Joseph-Louis Lagrange (I should use the ZZ Top song "La Grange" as a segue into number theory, no?). Here is where the story goes a little sideways. Sophie took on the name of Lagrange's former student, Monsieur LeBlanc, and submitted what must have been a head-turner of a paper, because it got the attention of Lagrange. He would eventually be the first person to find out the real identity of Sophie Germain. Her mathematics must have been captivating enough to override the gender prejudice of the time, as he took her under his wing and began to mentor her.

In 1801, Carl Friedrich Gauss, one of the most highly regarded mathematicians of all time, published one of his landmark textbooks, *Disquisitiones Arithmeticae*, a book chock full of number theory goodness. Guess who ate that up? Sophie, who was only a year older than Gauss. Her mathematical fate was sealed with her rightful excitement about that book—Fermat's last theorem would eventually become her obsession. Using again her *nom de plume*, Monsieur LeBlanc, she began corresponding with Gauss in 1804 about some of her own work in this history-laden branch of mathematics called number theory. Yet Gauss, for reasons we do not know, never responded to that first missive. It would be foolhardy to write Gauss off due to this initial dismissiveness—as we shall see.

In 1807, during the Napoleonic Wars, the French were occupying the German town of Braunschweig, where Gauss was living. Sophie, feeling pangs of anxiety, began to envision an Archimedes-type fate for Gauss. So she summoned the help of General Pernety, a family friend, to ensure Gauss would be safe. Pernety, after contacting the battalion chief in that town, assured Germain that Gauss was indeed safe and not to worry. However, Gauss was puzzled as to why Sophie Germain's name was involved in this query of safety. Months later, Gauss would find out the identity of Monsieur LeBlanc through a confession that was probably awkward and embarrassing for Sophie. Gauss's reply, in a long letter, is one of the greatest correspondence pieces in math history—and punctuates this story with an ending appropriate to a great tearjerker film:

How can I describe my astonishment and admiration on seeing my esteemed correspondent M. Le Blanc metamorphosed into this celebrated person . . . when a woman, because of her sex, our customs and prejudices, encounters infinitely more obstacles than men in familiarizing herself with [number theory's] knotty problems, yet overcomes these fetters and penetrates that which is most hidden, she doubtless has the noblest courage, extraordinary talent, and superior genius.

While the passage acknowledges the extraordinary talents of Sophie, it also delivers a gut punch with all the doors that were closed in her mathematical journey. A 2017 *Scientific American* article by Evelyn Lamb beautifully extrapolates the melancholy that was nested in Gauss's letter and claims Sophie as the first female research mathematician. And this despite having no easy access to the people and resources that are critical to work effectively in that field. Candles and thin blankets are how Sophie started her lifetime love affair with mathematics, and "candles and thin blankets" also became a metaphor for the courage, resilience, and feistiness that would have allowed her to be *infected* by mathematics.

Sophie Germain did some groundbreaking work in number theory, and specifically in the area of trying to prove Fermat's last theorem. However, she was equally talented in the world of physics and did groundbreaking work in the field of elasticity and how metal responds to stress. The construction of the Eiffel Tower is directly linked to Sophie's work here. Like with math, Sophie was snubbed by the scientific community—even though she won a prize in 1821 for her work, she could not attend the ceremony because of sexist restrictions. Ironically, that very same institute that barred Sophie now has an annual prize in her name—and of the nearly one hundred streets in Paris named after mathematicians, only one bears the name of a woman: Rue Sophie Germain.

Sophie died in 1831 from breast cancer. And, like Ramanujan, she worked on math right until the very end, publishing a paper of a partial solution to Fermat's last theorem. In so many ways, Sophie Germain is not just a French heroine, or even a mathematical heroine. She is just a hero. Period.

A STORY OF INDIGENOUS INNOVATION

In 2010, I received a slingshot to everything written in this chapter. I probably wouldn't have encountered or learned about all the richness and color of math history if it wasn't for the accelerant events of that year. The first evidence of my passion for math history and for tying it to equity occurred in that summer, as a workshop I gave on fusing these complementary ideas—Searching for Equity.

The words *searching* and *chasing* are almost identical for me. They represent constant learning and the needed recalibration of math's purpose in our lives. The resulting connected twists and turns, personal and professional, have brought me to the most satisfying part of life—*after* the age of fifty-five. And I have YouTube to thank.

I am going to apologize right off the bat. I have no memory of how I found *the video* on YouTube. I will be honest: when I first started watching videos on this platform, it was mostly for college humor—you know, stuff like cats flying off of ceiling fans and people eating ghost peppers. What can I say? YouTube was only for entertainment in the early days. Luckily, TEDx talks were appearing on this growing medium at the same time. Soon, cats and their battle with centripetal force were replaced with more academic indulgences. And, around 2009 or 2010, I came across this life-changing video: "Ron Eglash: The Fractals at the Heart of African Designs."

In 1988, Ron Eglash had his life-changing moment, made only more powerful by the randomness that shadows our lives. He was studying aerial photographs of the thatched roofs of Tanzanian houses. When Eglash studied the photographs, he noticed geometric patterns of circles within circles. As someone who had experience as a computer engineer in Silicon Valley, Eglash must have been excited at the prospects of what he saw. The calculations proved him right. Fractals. Ron Eglash had found his personal rabbit. The chase was on. His flourishing career in the field of ethnomathematics was born.

Eglash's TEDx talk took place two decades later. The fruits of his findings were on proud display. His own theory that fractals might be a general Indigenous design element were quashed early. Only Africa had this unique mathematical footprint—and it was *throughout* Africa. In his talk, Eglash rightfully opens with Cantor, the father of infinity, to link that concept to the self-similarity in fractals that *goes on and on and on and on . . .*

There is a wonderful lightness to the whole talk, and Eglash tells the audience that he got a Fulbright scholarship to go to Africa and ask people why they were building fractals. "Which," he says, "is a great job if you can get it." As he would find out, fractals were everywhere in Africa. In the architecture. In the clothing. In the pottery. In the social hierarchies. Fractals were in every facet of African life. They truly were at the heart of all their designs.

Naturally, as a high school math teacher, I was blown away by this talk. I knew so much about fractals and their occurrence in nature and in our own anatomy/physiology—it turns out a healthy heartbeat is *fractal, not regular!* Before Eglash's astounding find in Africa, the mathematician who was most associated with fractals was the late Benoit B. Mandelbrot. He had such a warm and disarming phrase for the mathematical complexity of fractals: "the art of roughness."

The same year that I gave a modest workshop on math equity, Mandelbrot gave his one and only TEDx talk. Sadly, he would pass away that same year. His opening words hide neither his frailty nor his youthful passion for mathematics:

> Thank you very much. Please excuse me for sitting; I'm
> very old. (Laughter) Well, the topic I'm going to discuss is
> one which is, in a certain sense, very peculiar because it's

very old. Roughness is part of human life forever and forever, and ancient authors have written about it. It was very much uncontrollable, and in a certain sense, it seemed to be the extreme of complexity, just a mess, a mess, and a mess. There are many different kinds of mess. Now, in fact, by a complete fluke, I got involved many years ago in a study of this form of complexity, and to my utter amazement, I found traces—very strong traces, I must say—of order in that roughness. And so today, I would like to present to you a few examples of what this represents. I prefer the word roughness to the word irregularity because irregularity—to someone who had Latin in my long-past youth—means the contrary of regularity. But it is not so. Regularity is the contrary of roughness because the basic aspect of the world is very rough.

The blind spot around fractals—the origin of their practical application in Africa—was now removed. Sure, the cell phones we have today could not exist without the invention of fractal antennas by Nathan Cohen in the early '90s, but the complete, colorful, and equitable story could not exist without the contributions of African culture. When I told this story in my workshop, there was a group of people sitting in the back that I had not expected. It was about a dozen or so Black students from a nearby summer camp. While I was flattered they were there, their faces suggested rightful skepticism. They could not have known I was going to show Eglash's entire TEDx talk. What happened after my workshop was a turning point inside an already turning point—yeah, life is truly fractal.

Since my workshop was during the first session, there was a lunch break after. I went to the cafeteria to get a sandwich and just sit down at a table to read the copy of *The Crest of the Peacock* that I had brought. That book follows me everywhere. It has numerous coffee stains, as well as traces of muffin and toast particles on many pages. I like that my favorite math history book has the detritus of professional development travels. Around ten minutes later, many of the students who had sat in the back of my presentation now approached me during my lunch. They sat down. They didn't even ask. *I was already excited by this break in etiquette.* The students huddled around me. Their eyes were lit up. We didn't need to exchange words. I knew what was going on and what was about to happen—their curiosity was stoked and a probe into knowing more about their mathematical roots was about to commence. Identity. Mathematics can trigger the search for it. That is why we need to be passionate about diversity, equity, inclusion, and culturally responsive curriculum—it's just better mathematical content and pedagogy. Not just for students who have been traditionally marginalized, but for all students.

Yes. And that is exactly what happened, with their visible emotion in the moment. Brighter smiles joined brighter eyes. This was the rarest of moments. Students chasing down a teacher—in the summer—to learn more about mathematics. The capability of Black students in mathematics has always been there. We, as educators, intentionally or not, have just not paid enough attention, collectively, to their talent and enthusiasm. Their identity and belonging in mathematics have rarely been anchored in something as great as Africa fractals, but I inadvertently offered that anchor to those students. It would be the last time my actions were accidental. I now would keep an abridged version of the story you just read ready to be told. Anytime and anywhere.

A STORY OF MIRACLES

THE MAN WHO KNEW INFINITY

In a paper appearing soon after he had unearthed it, Andrews styled his find "The Lost Notebook." Its discovery, mathematician Emma Lehmer was moved to say, was "comparable to the complete sketch of the tenth symphony of Beethoven."

If you read the above passage from Robert Kanigel's *The Man Who Knew Infinity: The Life of Genius Ramanujan*, without even knowing the story and its context, the words feel like a culmination of events, especially with a lofty, and well-deserved, comparison to a famous find in classical music. Some of the greatest stories have endings that feel complete and satisfying. A familiar "The End" from childhood is all there is left to say. Or . . . is it?

The greatest stories often don't have endings. Punctuation marks like a period or an exclamation mark cannot really contain their longevity. A modest and improbable comma is the symbolic replacement for "To be continued . . . "

You should also remember, I made a short but important reference to the last years of Ramanujan's life and George Andrews in chapter three. There is a beautiful continuation of the story here that connects Emma Lehmer's emotional appraisal of Andrew's discovery—a seemingly plausible conclusion—to a future that will begin almost *precisely when* the words you are reading will be first available. Sounds cryptic, right? I haven't even given you the extended story, and yet already I am suggesting that these added chapters will be leading to a critical event, possibly in the realm of math education. Yeah, I got ahead of myself. But storytelling, like mathematics, is messy and sometimes out of order. Where we might fail in order, we often make up in enthusiasm. Okay, let me put the horse before the cart . . .

In the summer of 2020, Amy Alznauer contacted me on Twitter and said, "I'd love to chat sometime soon about a conference idea I have."

Truth be told, I didn't know who she was, but her short query intrigued the hell out of me. A Google search revealed that she teaches at Northwestern University, has an MFA in creative writing, and is the author of the children's book *The Boy Who Knew Infinity*—a story, *unsurprisingly*, about Ramanujan when he was a little boy.

Hmmm. Have you put a piece of my puzzled story together yet? Well, not soon after, I found out that Amy Alznauer is the *daughter* of George Andrews! Wow. Full stop. That's an organic and surprising twist, don't you think? I had no idea! Almost like fate, as if the universe has some mysterious GPS system to direct people to those who will act as inflection points in our lives (really was tempted to insert a calculus joke here).

George Andrews not only discovered Ramanujan's lost gem of mathematics, but he would have been the only mathematician on the planet to recognize the work in these notes—mock theta functions—as his dissertation was on that very subject! The magnitude of that coincidence cannot be overstated. In 1976, Andrews visited his number theorist friend, Lucy Slater, in England. She told him about some math notes and papers that were part of the estate of another number theorist, George Neville Watson, and were kept at the Wren Library at Trinity College. Amy Alznauer, who was five years old at the time, said her father wasn't expecting to find much. Wow. What a complete underestimation of the mathematical gold that lay in this box—the now revered lost notes of Ramanujan. Oh yes, one more important event happened in this story: George Andrews fell into the River Cam while punting (a punt being a flat-bottomed boat used in shallow waters). But that's not the important event, as it yielded little more than some drenched clothes and understandable embarrassment. The importance was for a little five-year-old girl: Amy Alznauer.

That splash, in Amy's own words, became a metaphorical trumpet to announce to the world that her father had reached back in time, with the findings of the Lost Notebook, and connected with the brilliant and magical mind of Ramanujan. Of course, at the time, the splash simply meant that her father had fallen into the river. But now, that sound also represents the impact Ramanujan and his mathematics would have on Amy—especially the lesson that storytelling must be at the heart of teaching mathematics. One of the slides she created for an NCTM-sponsored panel discussion on "Connecting Mathematics and Science Through Children's Literature and Storytelling," back in early 2021, had these critical outcomes about when stories and mathematics come together. Think about all the stories in this chapter and other ones you have come across in this book as you reflect on the bullet points:

- Stories can challenge ideas of who a mathematician is.
- What counts as doing math?
- Stories launch culturally embedded explorations.
- Stories foster compassion for math struggles and inspire perseverance.
- Stories read with others create metaphors and build a common language for classrooms and communities.

Circling back to Amy's initial reason for contacting me—an idea for a math conference. During our buoyant conversations about mathematics filled with childlike wonder, we *infected* each other with our love for mathematics, history, and stories. So, sure enough, our destined entanglement through social media eventually led to a meeting with NCTM, including Trena Wilkerson, the current president. The idea to create a conference that bridges the world of children's literature and publishing with math/math education found an enthusiastic partner—the biggest math organization in North America!

I am honored to be part of the Program Committee for the NCTM 2022 Annual Meeting and Exposition, where the emergent theme of storytelling will be officially unveiled and celebrated.

ONE MATHEMATICS, MANY VOICES

What started out as mere wide-eyed conversations between a couple of kindred math spirits are now evolving into ensuring that the stories of mathematics, the stories of teachers, and the stories of our students form a new vision and journey in mathematics. A vision that is not only more inclusive and expansive, but that also simply opens us more to the pillars of wellness. Stories don't transmit data. Stories carry energy. That energy can lead us to thinking about mathematics in healthier ways for all of us.

The power of Amy's story comes from the power of mathematics and the power of curiosity. Her personal tale of how she became spellbound by mathematics lies squarely in its history. Mathematics lies in wait for all of us. And where it has the most colors, crevices, and contours is in this magical labyrinth. In 2020, the power of mathematical stories led me to create this slide, which I use in all my keynotes, workshops, and presentations.

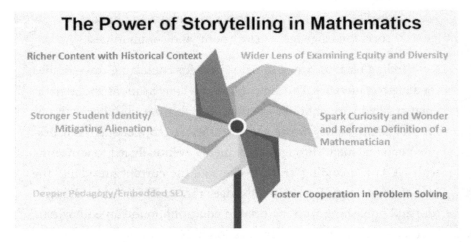

The Power of Storytelling in Mathematics

Richer Content with Historical Context

Wider Lens of Examining Equity and Diversity

Stronger Student Identity/ Mitigating Alienation

Spark Curiosity and Wonder and Reframe Definition of a Mathematician

Deeper Pedagogy/Embedded SEL

Foster Cooperation in Problem Solving

Five magical stories rooted in the history of mathematics, projecting toward the future. These stories have strong personal connections to my own journey as an educator and have become unmistakable benchmarks of my passion for humanizing mathematics. Falling down the Coxeter rabbit hole was my path here. I started in the twentieth century and then just went back from there. After that, it's all a blur of spontaneous searching. I feel like a pinball in a dizzying machine of spinners, ramps, lights, and bells, at the mercy of randomness. Good travel involves winging it. Time travel through math history is no different. Move with the current of your own flow.

And by *involving* yourself in any combination of these stories, you most definitely will embark on a unique journey of mathematics. We might bump into each other, and we might not. Both situations are comforting. The most important thing is that you enter this enormous maze of math history. I wouldn't even bother trying to sprint through it. You won't make a dent in what exists here. Rather, pace yourself, like how you might do a wine tour in Napa Valley, with its over five hundred wineries. You would give yourself a luxurious low-gear speed to hit the recommended three to five wineries in a day. The sipping would be naturally slow. Conversations would flow. You would be getting to know the people who work there. Listen to their grape stories. Savor.

Mathematics has *several thousand wineries.* It is not only Napa, Tuscany, Bordeaux, and other big-name regions. It is also about Fredericksburg, Texas, the second-biggest wine region in the United States. It is also about the Lavaux vineyards in Switzerland, one of the top rated in the world. Fredericksburg and Lavaux are symbolic of the beautiful surprises that await you inside. It will not matter which grapes of mathematics you've tasted. All that will matter is that you stayed.

8

THROUGH THE
LOOKING GLASS

**If you don't know where you are going,
any road will take you there.**
—Lewis Carroll

The idea of roads less traveled has come up a few times in this book already. Usually, however, this has involved larger, life-altering events in the lives of various people in this book—including me. I am certain many of you have a story or two about the forks in your own life's roads. Robert Frost's famous quote is now a mantra for the curious and courageous. But how does this apply to math?

It could mean experiencing a different solution to a math question, depending on the problem-solving path you take. The square problem that I shared at the beginning of the book, with my student Yanna providing truly imaginative insight, has a total of five completely unique solutions—at least! That is *not* how I am going to present the idea of mathematical adventure here. While the different solution paths to the same answer are quite interesting, that is not what this chapter is about. No. What I have become interested in—quite accidentally, over time—is *deconstructing the question*. To look at math questions differently, through a new perspective and purpose. *Through the Looking Glass*.

Perhaps subconsciously inspired by deconstructed cooking, where traditional dishes are given a makeover while still preserving the essence of the dish, I started looking at math questions with the same quirky creativity. Was there something new that could come out of them if I explored them in unfamiliar ways? Sure enough, some high school-level concepts started dropping down to middle school, and became not only easier to understand because of this approach, but also more interesting. Naturally embedded in *chasing a new recipe for old problems* is becoming a storyteller. We never know what can happen to us when we desire new roads, new adventures, and new math moments. But I do know this: that living for newness is part of the spiritual wellness pillar—extending right down to small, ordinary math questions.

Many years ago, I used to go up to a friend's cottage every summer. Because of the proximity of the cottage to where I was living, there were, even just traveling on highways and major roads, various ways to get from point A (my home) to point B (his cottage). The first two years, I simply took the fastest route horizontally and vertically to get there. However, in subsequent visits, I took more adventurous and time-consuming routes that combined "smaller chunks" of horizontal and vertical travel. My rationale? To simply drive through different parts of my province and see new terrain, vistas, towns, and hamlets.

On one such trip, I stopped at a town in Sunderland. I stopped because I saw an endearing homemade sign that said, "Fresh Baked Pies." I think one is obligated as part of a road trip to stop when those three words are charmingly hand-painted on well-worn wood. It's not only good pies that await, but friendly conversation with the proud bakers. This is a ritual that has played out for decades all over the backroads of North America. Those unspoiled and unpredictable linkages to savory food and conversation.

The apple and strawberry-rhubarb pies that I had in Sunderland almost thirty years ago are, still to this day, the best I have ever tasted. And I wouldn't have found this gem if I hadn't been curious and patient enough to *not take* the fastest and most common route. As is often the case, the most serviceable paths in life are all too often littered with mediocrity. If I would have kept taking the same route, the only thing that would have defined my trip was predictability. Sure, there are times when we want that reliable and definite outcome. Road trips shouldn't be one of them. Friends and good music pair well with memories of travel surprises.

In 1991, one of my favorite bands, Ireland's the Waterboys, released their landmark album, *Fisherman's Blues*. In "Strange Boat," the words "strange/strangest" appear in all but two lines of that song. That is seventeen times. Every noun, like boat, shore, crew, wind, star, etc., is described as being strange. Everything is unfamiliar. The whole journey in this strange boat—*lifeboat*—is dancing with the unknown. If I wanted to make a soundtrack for why and how this book was written, that song just might be my first choice. Then again, I don't think I had a choice. I am chasing one wonderfully strange rabbit. Sorry, *we* are chasing.

One of the reasons for my attraction to mathematics—and what gives it so much color—is that it is full of surprises! But I soon came to realize that those surprises occur more often if we look at mathematical ideas and problems in ways that are a little unconventional, slightly twisted, and just a little *strange*.

Looking glass is an antiquated term for a mirror. As a lark, reflect an exponent question into "a mirror" for your students. I know, I am playing a little fast and loose with the actual reflection. Just go with me on this one—and give me plenty of slack. Maybe you well get responses like, "Why would you do that?" Let them stew in the nonsensicalness of it all. And then surprise them with the question of "So . . . what's the answer?"

I am using a mirror and its literal definition to highlight what the phrase *through the looking glass* has come to mean—*the opposite of what is normal or expected.*

$$3^4 \qquad\qquad {}^4 3$$

$$= 3 \cdot 3 \cdot 3 \cdot 3 \qquad = 3^{3^{3^3}}$$

$$= 81$$

$$3^{76255974 84987}$$

= A number with over 3 million digits!

Did you expect that? Did you know that? That there is "life" beyond exponentiation? Up until a few years ago, I certainly did not! I only stumbled upon it when I went down the rabbit hole of trying to understand BIG numbers—numbers that make googol (one hundred zeros) look quite scrawny. The image on the left is familiar to every middle school student (should it be familiar earlier . . . hmm?). But what is happening in the image on the right? What do you think? What would your students think? Our gut mathematical instincts are often bypassed for the clear definition/explanation. We are skipping the messy middle. In exponentiation, we wrote four copies of 3 with multiplication signs. In tetration, we wrote four copies of 3 as a tower of exponents. We leveled up!

I could have listed tetration as a fact and it still would have been interesting. But I wanted to play with the odd positioning of the "4" and bring in the idea of a mirror image as a quirky amplifier of the final surprise—for which I'd seeded anticipation right from the get-go. The combination of not knowing where I could be going *and* wanting to know where I could be going is what I like to think of as getting curiosity-drunk!

As we discussed in chapter four, we can't find our edges if we don't get lost. As such, perhaps we should chart different directions and unexplored paths to get to our mathematical destinations in our classrooms. It might take us longer—which would be a *great thing*—but we just might discover some delectable mathematical goodies that can braid together our factual, procedural, and conceptual fluency.

And coming off the wind of the previous chapter, it is historical fluency that knots them all together. Might the exploration of mathematics have a similar road map, where seeking—*chasing*—unpredictability isn't compromised by time constraints or roads most taken? The Sunderland pies of mathematics await us all. The following are some of my favorite diversions, and hopefully you will see that each one of them was able to harvest richer connections to mathematics by approaches that were surprising, unconventional, and joyful. The one that I want to show first is the idea that opened this book. Yes. I didn't forget!

So, quickly recapping, I listed numbers that were divisible by 24. But I was only interested in the first two of those, 24 and 48. As you might remember, *I didn't care much* for 72 or 96! Sure, I could have stated the fact that all prime numbers squared, less one, are divisible by 24. But that would have been rather dry. Instead, I hemmed and hawed my way through some self-constructed narrative designed to invoke some, yes, strangeness. It was intentional that I acted weird right from the beginning. I think I was shooting for a Willy Wonka meets Dr. Seuss vibe—seriously! The proofs that follow for this lesser-known mathematical fact are courtesy of Matt Parker of Numberphile. Parker, also being a stand-up comedian, is my gold standard for trying to inject lightness, silliness, and humor in the presentation of sometimes very challenging mathematics.

BEAUTY AND THE BEAST

As you are going to see, there are two proofs that show that, after 3, every prime number squared minus one equals a number with 24 as a factor. I even love the sound of the mild implausibility of pairing squared primes, and it being related to a "chunky" number like 24.

I love how Matt Parker approaches this. He first starts off by saying that all prime numbers above 2 are either $6k + 1$ or $6k - 1$ (k is any number greater than zero). Try it! It's just a mathematically fancy way of saying primes, by not having 6 as a factor, don't have 2 *and* 3 as a factor. Also, as Parker realized, k could be odd or even. So, he made two cases for each situation.

This becomes our starting point for the proof! Let us walk through the chart.

| 6K+1 | k Even | k=2m | 6(2m)+1 | 12m+1 | $(12m+1)^2$ | $144m^2+24m$(+1) * |
| | k Odd | k=2m+1 | 6(2m+1)+1 | 12m+7 | $(12m+1)^2$ | $144m^2+24m+48$(+1) * |

* Is divisible by 24!

| 6K−1 | k Even | k=2m | 6(2m)−1 | 12m−1 | $(12m-1)^2$ | $144m^2-24m$(+1) * |
| | k Odd | k=2m+1 | 6(2m+1)−1 | 12m+5 | $(12m+5)^2$ | $144m^2+120m+24$(+1) * |

After stating the two versions of prime numbers after 2, he begins to unpack them. However, it becomes apparent that k could be odd or even. As such, there will be a total of four cases to check at the end. In column three, the value of k is inserted. Column four is the simplified form after some light expanding. In column five, this expression is ready to be squared. After expanding, the underlined part is divisible by 24 and a "+1" either occurs or can be extracted out from the resulting constant (i.e., 49 = 48 + 1). So yes indeed, every prime number greater than 3 squared is just one more than a number that has 24 as a factor! This might be the only time where there is some suspense as to multiplying out binomials. While I liked Matt Parker's proof—I, like him, love all things in the weeds of algebra—his friend gave him a proof that was more elegant. Remember what we were trying to prove. Another way of saying that is that every prime number squared minus one will have a factor of 24.

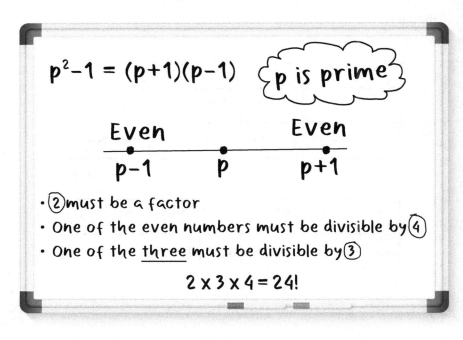

So, the first mathematical truth that hits us is that 2 must be a factor in a string of three consecutive numbers. In our case, these numbers are labelled $p - 1$, p, and $p + 1$. All even numbers are divisible by 2—and they *surround* p, which is prime. Also, one of those even numbers must be divisible by 4. Staying with that line of thinking, in a string of three numbers, one of them will be divisible by 3. *Et voilà!* (I am dedicating that French exaltation to my kindred math spirit, Luc Goudreault). Proof is the gold standard in mathematics. And it is so heavily dependent on the language of algebra. It's not just logical. It is unapologetically beautiful.

Could you have ever imagined the amount of cool mathematical reasoning that lay ahead of the first sentence in this entire book—"24 is a factor of 288"? No. But, that is the point. I am hoping you were curious as to how this quirky, tiny story would unfold. Weird introduction. Logical conclusion. Let's move on to more of the same!

CAUGHT IN A CIRCLE

Every number after 27 can be written as a sum with just 5s and 8s! Some of you might know this fact, but imagine making that proclamation to middle school kids. Pretty sure you are going to get more than a few skeptics. Is this true? Can we prove it—and prove it at a level for kids to understand? Affirmative to all. The best way to start is to follow students' instinct to see if this does hold true for, let's say, the first twenty or so numbers.

28	5+5+5+5+8	36	5+5+5+5+8+8
29	5+8+8+8	37	5+8+8+8+8
30	5+5+5+5+5+5	38	5+5+5+5+5+8
31	5+5+5+5+8+8+8	39	5+5+5+8+8+8
32	8+8+8+8	40	8+8+8+8+8
33	5+5+5+5+5+8	41	5+5+5+5+5+8+8+8
34	5+5+8+8+8	42	5+5+8+8+8+8
34	5+5+5+5+5	43	5+5+5+5+5+5+5+8

While many kids will now be believers—and experts at the 5s and 8s for multiplying—they should be interested in a general proof. Even the first number we tested, 28, when doubled to give 56, just means we will double our 5s and 8s. So, the double of every number is doable. Hmmm. There seems to be some repetition that is running deep in the current of this pattern. There surely is. It's modular arithmetic. That was my endgame here!

So, a quick lesson on "clock arithmetic." For example, if you divide 28 by 5, you get a remainder of 3. In modular arithmetic language, that would be written like 28 is congruent to 3(mod 5). It's no different in saying that 1:00 p.m. on a clock looks like 1:00 a.m. on a clock—they both have one "leftover" (the clock has a modulus 12). The nifty proof below of our mod 5 situation was shared by @SciencePundit on Twitter.

28	$4 \cdot 5 + 8 \cdot 1$	$3 \pmod 5$
29	$1 \cdot 5 + 3 \cdot 8$	$4 \pmod 5$
30	$6 \cdot 5$	$0 \pmod 5$
31	$3 \cdot 5 + 3 \cdot 8$	$1 \pmod 5$
32	$4 \cdot 8$	$2 \pmod 5$

Any other number that needs to be obtained can just have some multiple of 5 added to those in the chart (depending on their particular *congruence*). If you wanted to build, for example, the number 97, that is 2(mod 5), as 97 is two more than 95. So, go to the number 32 and figure out what needs to be added to get to 97—which is 65. Add thirteen 5s (65) to get 97. The problem of 5s and 8s is captivating on its own, but I wanted to create a *false finish line*—that students would be satiated with just having "enough" examples to believe that you can express every number after 28 with multiples of 5 and/or multiples of 8. That they would think that the question was dealt with and over. Not only did we get to a nice piece of important mathematics, but we've gently implanted the idea of trying to prove things.

FINAL JEOPARDY

One of the more inclusive ideas in math education has been the open-ended question: What do you notice and what do you wonder? This is the epitome of a safe and encouraging math question that gives multiperson perspective into unpacking a math idea. A while back, I came across a tough question that definitely would have benefited from this collaborative approach. The question was to draw all the *unique* geometric figures that contain exactly *four lattice points*, such that there are *exactly two different distances* between all the points.

I came up with the square and rhombus, but then got stuck—really stuck. The thick lines represent one particular length, and the thin lines another. All conditions met, right? I did come up with one more after a while, but I only produced half the answers.

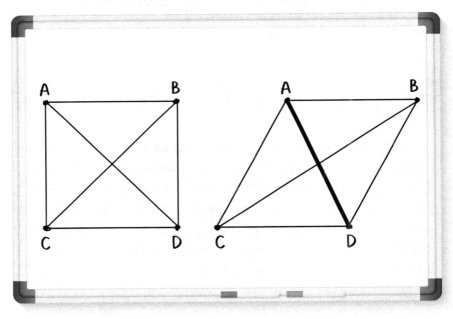

So I thought, how about giving the *answer to the question*—a la *Jeopardy*—and have students in a similar spirit, with lots of open dialogue, come up with the actual question. It is easier, but still not as easy as you might think. But it will bring students to examining a math idea with a complete 180-degree perspective.

Here are all the answers. Now imagine asking students to solve for . . . the question itself.

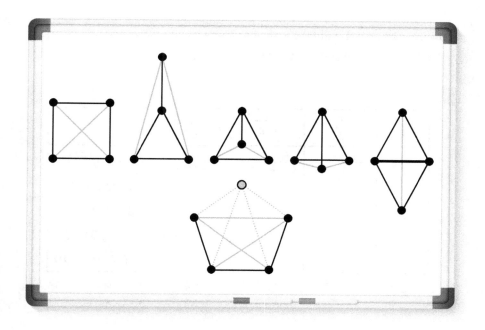

A TRANSCENDING GAME

This idea of doing some literal reverse engineering of humdrum algebra comes again via my favorite math website, Numberphile. This time it is Australian mathematician Simon Pampena. Like all the hosts at that delicious YouTube channel, Simon introduces mathematics with a disarming cocktail of relaxed body language, reassuring smiles, and trademark Numberphile humor and silliness. While this game that we are going to play will take you right to the apex of high school algebra, feel free to hop off anywhere, as this is a K to 12 trip through some of the most important numbers in mathematics. It is much like an amusement park where you have to be so tall to ride some of the more challenging rides. Some of these numbers require you to know a certain level of mathematics.

Let's set the rules of the game. We are allowed to add, subtract, multiply, and use exponents (for our purposes we will only do things like squaring or taking the square root). The goal of the game is to write down a number and, using the rules of the game, try to get that number to *zero*. I will take a similar route to what Pampena does, and let's see if you can see what the endgame is here.

5	$\dfrac{2}{3}$	$\sqrt{2}$	$i = \sqrt{-1}$	$\sqrt{3} + \sqrt{5}$
$5-5$	$3 \cdot \dfrac{2}{3} - 2$	$(\sqrt{2})^2 - 2$	$5-5$	$(\sqrt{3} + \sqrt{5})^2$ $= 3 + \sqrt{30} + 5$ $= 8 + \sqrt{30}$ $= 8 + \sqrt{30} - 8$ $= (\sqrt{30})^2 - 30$
$\cdot \; -5$	$\cdot \; \times 3$ $\cdot \; -2$	$\cdot \; sq$ $\cdot \; -2$	$\cdot \; sq$ $\cdot \; +1$	$\cdot \quad sq$ $\cdot \quad -8$ $\cdot \quad sq$ $\cdot \quad -30$

So, as I tabulated my game moves at the bottom of the chart—all the allowed rules—the numbers that we selected all could be reduced to zero! Even the one at the end, which might have raised some doubt, was able to be steered toward our target number of zero with some more moves.

Well, here is the reveal of what is going on. Look at the chart that follows. If you replace all the numbers we selected with x, then we have created algebraic equations! And here is the key part: we could solve all of them! Equations that have solutions to this "game" are called algebraic numbers. Even the last one (I expanded and simplified to show it is a quartic equation) yields algebraic numbers.

$x-5=0$	$3x-2=0$	$x^2-2=0$	$x^2+1=0$	$(x^2-8)^2-30=0$
				$x^4-16x^2+34=0$
Integer	Rational	Irrational	Complex	Irrational

This is where I am going to stop the game. Do you see any specific numbers absent from the one I gave you? They are famous. Two historically relevant numbers—π and e. These numbers, if selected, and using the basic rules of our game, cannot be taken down to zero. They are called *transcendental numbers*. Already belonging to the lore of numbers, now they reveal themselves as being *resistant* to benign solutions to algebraic equations. Later in the video, Pampena uses Euler's famous identity to prove that π is indeed transcendental. A lovely commentary comes at the end of the video, as Pampena examines the detritus of work with a satisfied expression of delight. He says, "The tricky stuff is where all the awesome mathematics is." It sure is, Simon. It sure is. What have we called this tricky stuff? The "messy middle," right? Tricky equals magic. Thank you, Simon, for taking us on a scenic tour of algebra with this backward game.

THE STRANGE BANK

I can't remember the year, but there was this time that I was teaching calculus and a grade 11 math course at the same time. And, quite as a fluke, I saw an opportunity to use the compound interest topic to flesh out the transcendental number e, through an implicit idea of a limit. It sounds way more complicated than it is. To make the idea more interesting, I started off with the idea that there is a fictitious bank of generosity that offers an interest rate of 100 percent. To add to the strangeness, I told my students that the most we can invest in this bank is one dollar, and the longest we can leave our investment in the bank is one year. I believe I had set up the question to sound so absurd that they were curious as to what the ramifications of these strange ideas could be.

The only freedom they had was they could have their one-dollar investment compounded in any way they wanted to. So, we started with compounded yearly and went from there. The way that I would explain something compounded semiannually is that the bank will give you

Compound	i	n	
Annually	1	1	$A=1(1+1)^1=2^1=\$2$
Semiannually	0.5	2	$A=1(1+\frac{1}{2})^2=1.5^2=\$2.25$
Quarterly	0.25	4	$A=1(1+\frac{1}{4})^4=1.25^4=\$2.31$
Monthly	0.083	12	$A=1(1+\frac{1}{12})^{12}=1.083^{12}=\$2.60$
Daily	0.0027	365	$A=1(1+\frac{1}{365})^{365}=1.0027^{365}=\$2.67$
Hourly	0.00011	8760	$A=1(1+\frac{1}{8760})^{8760}=1.0001^{8760}=\$2.718$

interest twice a year, but it seems unfair they give you the whole lot each time. Makes sense to chop it in half. Same thing with quarterly: the bank will give you interest four times, but it will be divided by four. And so on.

After compounding semiannually, many students, rightly so, should anticipate a correlation between more compounding periods and a better return for your dollar investment. While there is an increase in quarterly, there might be some doubt now as to what this increase is all about. Jumping to monthly probably could now cause *doubt about their doubt*! However, what must be agreed upon is that this strange bank seems to be up to some strange things. There is much magic and wonder in the strange. Maybe we should take the Waterboys' "Strange Boat" out for a spin more often in the math classroom . . .

At hourly compounding, I wrote the result with a third decimal place—hoping that it might be noticed by as few people as possible. Hopefully only one, to add to the suspense of this story. It's like a joke. The best jokes for me are the ones that get boisterous laughter from everyone or from just one person. That lone voice of laughter in a large room gives the joke an edge and personality that is wholly unique. There is, however, a huge risk if nobody laughs. (I wouldn't know anything about that . . . *cough*.) But, in my experience with this problem, there have always been a few students who inquire about the inclusion of a third decimal place—especially since, for money, we generally don't deal with anything beyond whole cents.

The best way to answer this is to do one more investment. And to choose a unit of time that matches the ridiculousness of the problem, the smallest we use—second.

Compound	i	n	
Every Second	$\dfrac{1}{31536000}$ $=0.000000032$	31536000	$A=1(1+\dfrac{1}{31536000})^{31536000}$ $=(1.000000032)^{31536000}$ $=\$2.718$

Before you allow your students to pick their jaws up off the floor and fully realize that there is a limit here of 2.718, give a short little lesson on the historical importance of this magical number and drop this little bit of unknown information about when Google filed its IPO back in 2004. In an article written on CNET in April of that year, there is mention of why Google chose to have its IPO be 2.7 billion—you just had to scroll down to the eleventh paragraph!

> Another flourish involves the company's allegiance to its geeky roots: The amount of the $2.7 billion offering contains an inside joke for the math-minded. The exact offering, $2,718,281,828, is the product of "e" and $1 billion, where "e" is the base of the natural logarithm—a logarithm especially useful in calculus—and equals about 2.718281828.

Pretty sure you might not get a quirkier and more intriguing invite for students to take calculus. Remember the Dos Equis beer commercial with that distinguished older gentleman who says at the end, "Stay thirsty, my friends"? Well, for mathematics, that is also true when looking for new and innovative angles from which to approach conventional ideas. Stay thirsty—and stay quirky!

ANCIENT STAIRS

This problem is so front-loaded with problem solving and patterning that there is no way to anticipate the twist that comes at the end—especially when the problem terminates in a very familiar pattern. While this question works with any number of stairs, I use a particular picture of stairs that looks like it is somewhere in Asia. This is important in foreshadowing the red herring that lies ahead. The stairs have eight steps. A good idea might be just to show the picture of the eight stairs and nothing else—just let students stare at it and go fishing for questions! Even a question like, "How many stairs are there?" is a great one to start with. Maybe even ask how you might climb these stairs. At this point, you are hoping that it is a standard, boring *one step at a time*, which doesn't leave any room for anything interesting. Which is interesting in itself! Taking one step at a time means there is *only one way* to get up the stairs: 1 1 1 1 1 1 1 1.

And now, maybe in your best mock-sheepish expression, you introduce the idea that you can, if you want, take jumps of two. So now, you are allowed to either take one step or two steps when you ascend these eight steps. The question is, how many ways are there to climb these stairs? The instinct should always be to start writing out a few cases, even though this method as a strategy is laborious and prone to error in under- and overcounting. It is important to anchor ourselves as to what is meant by "different."

As with many questions that involve finding an answer involving *n* things, it is always worth considering the simplest case and going from there—start with one step. *Baby steps*, right?

There seems to be some triviality associated with this in the beginning. Be patient. A familiar pattern is soon revealed.

Steps	Possible Cases	Total Ways
1	(1)	1
2	(11), (2)	2
3	(111), (12), (2,1)	3
4	(1111), (112), (121), (211), (2,2)	5
5	(11111),(1112),(1121),(1211),(2111),(221),(212),(122)	8

You see the pattern? Fibonacci numbers! So, now we can continue the pattern of adding the two previous numbers to generate our next number, 13. That would be the answer for six steps. For seven it would be 21. And, finally, for eight steps, there would be 34 unique ways to climb them with the rule of taking one or two steps. Well, I guess that's a wrap . . . not!

The only problem is that, as we now know, Fibonacci was not the first person to discover the sequence named after him. That pattern was discovered by Hemachandra *earlier*. In Sanskrit poetry you have short (*laghu*) and long (*guru*) vowels. Laghu represents a syllable with a "length of one" and guru has a "length of two"—like the numbers in our stairs question. So one of the questions that was explored was how many different poems you could write with these two kinds of vowels. The resulting numbers were the same ones we got in our stairs question, and the same ones Fibonacci got with his rabbits!

This story is so compelling that Amplify, the company I work with in building narrative/storytelling into curriculum resources, created a whole interactive lesson with eye-catching visuals called, quite appropriately, the Poetry of Patterns. Rabbits. *Literally and figuratively.* They always seem to be lurking in math problems. Chasing soon becomes more of a personal, primal desire than a suggested motion or direction. I was nudged into investigating Coxeter over twenty years ago. Now there isn't enough time to fall down all the rabbit holes.

IS THIS DIVISIBLE BY 5?

Quite a few challenging number theory questions are accessible to even elementary students because of the inherent patterning found in many of these ostensibly challenging problems. The trick I found with this particular one was to lead the kids with boredom and me looking like the fool for trying to trip them up. Loading up kids with swagger and confidence in the beginning results in them actively, frantically even, trying to hurdle the wall that will eventually be presented to them.

I actually shared a question in this way for the first time in front of a fifth grade class in Coppell, Texas. I was visiting my friend Mary Kemper, who is the director of K to 12 mathematics in Coppell, back in May 2019. I asked her if there would be a chance I could do a "pop-up" lesson with one of the classes. Sure enough, an opportunity arose when May Voltz, a grade 5 teacher at the school, volunteered her period after lunch. I was told ahead of time that these kids were wonderfully attentive and curious. Game on!

After some warm-up questions, I wrote a number on the board and asked the wide-eyed kids if this number was divisible by 5. They quickly said yes. I wrote another one on the board. This had more digits. But understandably, there was no delay. At this point, the kids must have been thinking, *Why did this teacher come all the way from Canada and use his guest-teaching time doing such trivial divisibility?* I played the part of the fool perfectly. *For now, I was not as smart as a fifth grader!*

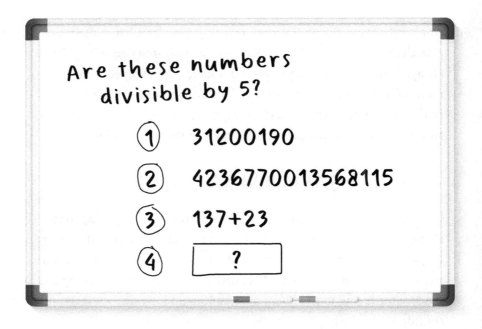

When I wrote the two numbers on line 3, there was only a slight pause, but again, all the hands went up signaling the affirmative. Before writing the mystery number in the box on line 4, I surveyed the class to ask if that answer to 137 + 23 depended on adding the numbers. Most kids said that you only have to add the final digits. I must have given an audible *hmmmph* before I went to the last number, reassuring them that it would fit in my rectangle and that I would still ask about divisibility by 5. Looking back, a perfect prop would have been to have a rabbit with me (*snickers to himself*).

I wish I'd had a camera when I wrote the number. The students' smiling confidence was replaced by unmistakable bewilderment. *What kind of number is that?* must have been the collective internal response.

$$3^{444} + 4^{333}$$

I asked the kids if anyone had a calculator—just to add more mischievous fun. And, just as quickly, I told them a calculator wouldn't help us! Some kids recognized the large numbers as exponents, but for the most part, there was uncertainty about what to do. I said that maybe we should learn what bases and exponents are, and perhaps start small until we get the hang of them. What I was hoping for was that students might notice a pattern with the last digit of each of the bases, 3 and 4.

$$3^1 = 3$$
$$3^2 = 3 \times 3 = 9$$
$$3^3 = 3 \times 3 \times 3 = 27$$
$$3^4 = 3 \times 3 \times 3 \times 3 = 81$$
$$3^5 = 3 \times 3 \times 3 \times 3 \times 3 = 243$$
$$3^6 = 3 \times 3 \times 3 \times 3 \times 3 \times 3 = 729$$

$$4^1 = 4$$
$$4^2 = 16$$
$$4^3 = 64$$
$$4^4 = 256$$
$$4^5 = 1024$$

From there, the class took hold of the problem and knew we just had to know what the last digit was for each of the large numbers—a small, affirming déjà vu moment that recalled the kind of thinking used for 137 + 23. With the patterning, we deduced that the first number ends in a 1 and the second number, a 4. As such, the final digits add to 5, and this massive number—that we didn't even need to know what it looked like in its entirety—was indeed divisible by 5. The moral of the story? Sometimes you can solve questions that your calculator cannot.

Getting kids into number theory early develops stronger number sense and better understanding of how numbers play, and sparks curiosity. In the previous question, we saw the necessity to unpack the pattern of the last digits of the bases 3 and 4. How about we just give the whole truckload from 2 to 9! (I heard 10 is just as *boring* as 5.)

Base	Expansion	"Base Code"
2	2,4,8,16,32,64,128,256,512,1024,2048	2486
3	3,9,27,81,243,729,2187,6561,19683	3971
4	4,16,64,256,1024,4096,16384	46
5	5,25,125,625,3125,15625	5
6	6,36,216,1296,7776,46656	6
7	7,49,343,2401,16807,117649	7931
8	8,64,512,4096,32768	8426
9	9,81,729,6561,59049	91

Playing with numbers 1 to 10 should also involve playing with bases with these fundamental numbers. Cool patterning emerges, and kids quickly graduate from multiplication to exponentiation. At which point, they can always go . . . *beyond*!

DOES 10 HAVE ANY FRIENDS?

In number theory, there are numbers that are described as social, amicable, and friendly. Seems like jolly good groups where there is some whimsical connection. While all three are interesting, I find friendly numbers to be the most amusing of the lot—and yes, it helps that their name has a familiar connotation, perhaps making people more curious as to the mathematical definition of *friendly numbers*. Right off the bat, all perfect numbers are friendly. Remember, perfect numbers are numbers whose proper divisors add up to the number in question. The reason they are all friendly is because they have the same *abundancy index.*

The abundancy index is calculated by adding all the divisors of a number (including the number itself) and dividing it by the number. Can you figure out what the abundancy index for perfect numbers will *always* be? Let's find the abundancy index for the first three perfect numbers.

Perfect Number	All Divisors	Abundancy Index
6	$\dfrac{1+2+3+6}{6} = \dfrac{12}{6}$	2
28	$\dfrac{1+2+3+7+14+28}{28} = \dfrac{12}{6}$	2
496	$\dfrac{1+2+4+8+16+31+62+124+248+496}{496}$	2

Just as a cool aside, perfect numbers have surprising facts attached to their "perfection." Did you know that adding the first two odd cubes—$1^3 + 3^3$—gives you the perfect number of 28? And, adding the first four odd cubes—$1^3 + 3^3 + 5^3 + 7^3$—gives you 496, the next perfect number! Number theory is the amusement park for mathematics, in my opinion.

So, are there any other friendly numbers? Meaning, numbers that share a different abundancy index. Yes, there are. Let me give you an example of a *very* long-distance kind of friendship. 24 has an abundancy index of 2.5 (yes, it can have decimals). Its friend is 91,963,648. That's nuts! I would have thought 24, twice a dozen, would have had a friend *waaaay* before this. Do you see how much fun you can have with writing your own narrative here with mathematics and "friendship"? Quite a bit. You could write a children's short story just about friendly numbers!

Which brings us to the most used and familiar base: 10. All the divisors of 10 are 1, 2, 5, and 10. Add them up and you get 18. Divide it by 10, and you get the abundancy index of 1.8. Surely, there is a friend out there somewhere (cue up the Rolling Stones' song "Waiting on a Friend"). As of right now, mathematicians believe that 10 is not a friendly number, and actually a solitary number. However, that is only a belief. There is no proof yet. And, just when we thought "we knew you so well, ten," you throw us this mathematical knuckleball—that there is a bit of dark romanticism in you.

ALGEBRA FOR MINORS

Remember back in chapter two when I shared that image of the guiding/cautionary words about the "challenge" problems? You might have assumed that Peter Harrison, who had a big hand in writing that extraordinary textbook, might have also written those words of wisdom. Nope. Those came from Peter Taylor. Let's dive deeply into one of his problems that is emblematic of his rabbit math!

Before I get to the problem that is a *classic hare tale* of mathematics, I want to tease out an idea that is related to Taylor's most unique portal into that thorny and often dry topic: algebra. When do students learn about solving simultaneous equations? High school, right? Well, there has been some minor disruption of this idea in recent years with emoji mathematics. You have probably seen them. Multiple equations with emojis as unknowns instead of traditional letters like x, y, and z.

What this has done to the idea of multiple equations is that it has the idea of more complex algebra down to middle school level. In my sixth grade Math Recess class that I streamed at Dexter Learning in 2020–2021—where I was allowed to teach *whatever* I wanted—many of these problems and their approaches have been shared there. The kids gobble up these quirky narratives. Including this one. I presented simultaneous equations in the more formal sense. My intent was not to go deeply into that concept. In fact, it was to just "pop by" and tell them they would come back here again—later. Endgame has always been to manufacture curiosity in my classes. My interest is more in where kids might end up. I don't need to witness it. In fact, I hope *I won't*.

$$a+b=8$$

I first gave the students this equation (Diophantine equations revisited, right?) and asked them to come up with numbers for *a* and *b* that made the statement true. *The list had the predictability I desired.* The "last" one offered up was that *a* could be 8 and *b* could be 0. And of course, we agreed that the answers for a and b could be "switched." First milestone reached. Zero can be a solution. I gave a sufficient pause before I said, "Any more?" Understandably, because negative numbers are artificially separated from positive numbers early, there was hesitation from the students. Eventually, a student did offer up numbers of 9 and −1. We plugged it in. It worked! (Those sociopathic negatives actually do play well with positives.) Naturally, we found more and more answers. The second milestone was within reach. I had asked for many different solutions to this equation. "Infinite" came back quickly.

Then I added a second equation:

$$a+b=8$$
$$a-b=4$$

Students, probably fueled by interest, solved this rather quickly—without algebra—in their heads. With the answer of $a = 6$ and $b = 2$ secure in our hands, I pretended that we were finished here. After all, we have our correct answer, right? But by now you might be able to sniff out math problems that don't necessarily terminate at the answer. *You just might be smelling those Sunderland pies!* I told students that in algebra, we are allowed to add our equations. So, I did so. There were no questions about what I wrote:

$$a+b=8$$
$$a-b=4$$
$$\overline{2a+0b=12}$$

We went on to solve $2a = 12$ and show that a is indeed equal to 6. I kid you not. A few of the students were in awe of that move—as legal it was. Comforted by having arrived at an answer and being thoroughly involved right from the beginning, the students were now curious about this thing called algebra.

But that was just an appetizer to pique the kids' fascination with the concept of algebra. What I have next for you is gold. Peter Taylor gold, to be exact.

In 2019, Christian Lawson-Perfect, one of the founders of the website Aperiodical, reached out to me to see if I wanted to participate in something called the Big Internet Math-Off. While the name of it sounds big and serious, Christian's aim was to make the competitive event quite lighthearted. There would be sixteen participants who would participate in round-robin format, with four mathematicians in each division. Contestants would pitch a math idea, and people would vote for one they found most interesting. *I knew beforehand that the pitch I was going to present would lose.* Even Peter Taylor might have scratched his head as to why I selected this idea. I am sure he would have remarked something like, "Sunil, surely you could have selected something a bit more exciting from all my problems?" I could have. But I wanted to use this once-in-a-lifetime platform to showcase the unassuming elegance and beauty of algebra in neglected places.

My pitch was called "The Correct Algebra Behind Mathematical Incorrectness." Sophie Carr's was "Bernoulli's Equation." When the final votes were tallied, Sophie had received 69 percent, and she went on to win the entire math-off! An interesting footnote is that Sophie messaged me and told me that her own son wanted to vote for my pitch. That kind of made my day. I started my pitch with a quote from one of my favorite writers and proceeded from there.

> # The moment one gives close attention to anything, even a blade of grass, it becomes a mysterious, awesome, indescribably magnificent world in itself.
> ## —Henry Miller

Mathematics is such a vast universe of BIG ideas. And many start there when trying to introduce people to the creative beauty of this subject. But, as alluded to in the Henry Miller quote, there is much magnificence and wonder in even the tiniest, unnoticed crevices of math—which often lead to rabbit holes of deeper exploration. One such "blade of grass" is in the somewhat obvious clumsiness of crossing out 6s below and still obtaining the correct answer. A bit of a fluke, wouldn't you say?

$$\frac{\cancel{6}4}{1\cancel{6}} = \frac{4}{1}$$

Okay, be honest. You are both curious as to where this is going and also, even being a lover of mathematics (hopefully), realize why I might have lost the math-off.

$$\frac{\cancel{9}5}{1\cancel{9}} = \frac{5}{1}$$

Hmmm. A second cancelling out mistake that yields a correct answer. The question that many of you are probably asking is: "Are there any more of these weird division questions?"

For two-digit fractions, there are two more. *Without* the power-up tool of algebra, you probably would never find them. Maybe some brute force with a little luck could do it. But I doubt it. My uncertainty in your ability to find them through trial and error is my bait for luring you into the world of algebra—through this tiny, mysterious, and rarely used door.

The fact that there are four instances where cancelling mistakes display the correct answer means there must be something happening to the arrangement of the digits that creates these rare situations. Algebra is the only tool that allows us to examine how these digits are dancing in this mathematical oddity. The first important thing is to isolate 10. After which, all the other numbers are given unknowns to describe the situation. Keep in mind, the a's get "canceled out," leaving b divided by c.

$$\boxed{\frac{6(10)+4}{10+6}} \rightarrow \boxed{\frac{10a+b}{10c+a} = \frac{b}{c}}$$

Since we are interested in what *b divided by c* looks like, it makes sense to find an expression that only has those unknowns—we should isolate *a*! This requires the skill of algebra. So, to "get rid of" our denominators, we multiply both sides by them. Being now in the logical world of algebra allows me this opportunity for a few screaming reminders.

$$(10c+a)(c) \cdot \frac{1a+b}{10c+a} = \frac{b}{c} \cdot (10c+a)(c)$$

There is no such thing as "cross multiplying"!

$$\cancel{(10c+a)}(c) \cdot \frac{1a+b}{\cancel{10c+a}} = \frac{b}{\cancel{c}} \cdot (10c+a)\cancel{(c)}$$

There is, however, such a thing as multiplying both sides by the exact same thing!

(*Deep inhale. Slow exhale . . .*). Brackets get multiplied. Terms with "*a*" are grouped on one side. Common factoring. Division. *Et voilà!*

$$\cancel{(10c+a)}(c) \cdot \frac{1a+b}{\cancel{10c+a}} = \frac{b}{\cancel{b}} \cdot (10c+a)(c)$$

$$c(10a+b) = b(10c+a)$$

$$10ac+bc = 10bc+ab$$

$$10ac-ab = 10bc-bc$$

$$a(10-b) = 9bc$$

$$a = \frac{9bc}{10-b}$$

Algebra has done its work. Now we must employ some creative thinking. Since there are four answers and an alphabet soup (relatively speaking) of an expression, it means we must examine "cases" where a certain unknown is given a value, and then we can see what is happening/not happening. *Remember,* a, b, *and* c *all have to be integers!*

Let c = 1.

$$a = \frac{9b}{10-b}$$

The only numbers that work are $b = 4$ and $b = 5$

$$\frac{\begin{matrix}b=4\\a=6\end{matrix}}{c=1} \rightarrow \boxed{\frac{64}{16}} \quad \boxed{\frac{95}{19}} \leftarrow \frac{\begin{matrix}b=5\\a=9\end{matrix}}{c=1}$$

Let c = 2. A nice surprise waits here!

$$a = \frac{18b}{20-b}$$

The only thing that works is $b = 5$ for a to have the integer solution of $\circled{6}$

$$\frac{\begin{matrix}a=6\\b=5\end{matrix}}{c=2} \rightarrow \frac{10(6+5)}{10(2)+6} \rightarrow \frac{65}{26} \rightarrow \frac{\cancel{6}5}{2\cancel{6}} \quad \frac{5}{2}$$

207

Okay, be honest. There isn't a snowball's chance in hell you would have found a number that even when reduced does not yield a whole number! It might have taken you years to locate this gold nugget—if not a lifetime. I actually don't even know what kind of strategy I would have employed to unearth these buried fractions. Oh yes. I have only shown you three. There is one more, and to honor the spirit of the book . . . go find it! You have everything you need. Just keep examining cases. If you get really stuck, email me!

Isn't mathematics one fun carnival ride after another? It can be. It should be. But, currently, it is not. Mathematics is a charming, whimsical, and mysterious diamond. Sometimes to see those vibrant colors bouncing around inside, we have to rotate it ever so slightly to get a new perspective. The question we just examined about how incorrect steps lead to correct solutions isn't limited to division. It also happens in radicals and exponents. But the algebra is challenging. Algebra has the power to extract truths from many mathematical problems—even the tiny, insignificant ones of lighthearted arithmetic mistakes. We can find these truths of various sizes and radiance simply by being willing to look at mathematics perhaps with a mischievous grin, one eye squinted, head cocked. In other words, like a child.

Graham Nash. Yes—*that Graham Nash*—narrated the opening of the Escher documentary I mentioned back in the first chapter. I think it is fitting they chose a musician who helped create some of the best music of the hippie/psychedelic generation with his band Crosby, Stills, Nash, and Young, to lift the mathematical art of Escher to the film's audience. Nash's words come from what all of us have done with Escher's work—just gaze at it: "Escher taught me to see differently," he said, "and I'm very thankful for that."

I'm pretty sure staring at Escher prints as a teenager while listening to music like Pink Floyd has allowed me to see things differently as well, but it's been a host of things. And at the top of that pile has been mathematics itself. All the problems I've shared here were the result of seeing things differently. My personal and professional goal with mathematics has always been to create curiosity—to examine life from various angles. It's not enough for me to just reflect on mathematics the way it was given to me. I feel obligated to refract it through the prism of my life and make it unconventional, strange, hypnotic, and weird. I guess we circle back to Escher and Pink Floyd, right? A book that claims to be a guide to elevating curiosity for something as lofty as building wellness needs to go right into the weeds of actual math problems, to reimagine them as little narratives of logical delight and surprise. The theory —> application road is worn out by its own predictability. Peter Taylor, author of, in my opinion, one of the greatest calculus books ever, *Calculus: The Analysis of Functions*, basically wrote the book on *application first and find theory later*. It's worth reminding ourselves of his simple but poignant question: "Mathematics is full of awe and wonder. Why don't we teach it that way?"

Good question, Peter. I don't know. But let's not wait to find out. Let's turn mathematics on its head. Let's take our students for a ride through the looking glass. They will appreciate us for doing that, and they will be thankful for the tasty "mathematical pies" we found and delighted in.

9

GO

**I'm going to live every
minute of it.**
—Joe Gardner (jazz musician from the movie *Soul*)

We are lucky. We get to see and *want to see* the world and our lives through the lens of mathematics. We should never take that for granted. Never. We get to see and experience colors, moods, and emotions that ripple effortlessly through main pillars of mathematical wellness—mental, social, emotional, and spiritual. Mathematics is wellness and has been the patient home for life's splendor since humans began to gaze up at the night sky. In the end, however, summoning this lifetime understanding and appreciation for all its abstract charm and enchantment requires a whole new belief in the potential of mathematics—for everyone. The quote below. I have used it before, around five years ago when I wrote the introduction to my first book, *Pi of Life: The Hidden Happiness of Mathematics*. It seems fitting to revisit it again to close out my last book. I mean, there is nothing left to say after exploring wellness, right? (It is okay to mix melancholia with realistic silliness.) It's finally time to go.

> Life's splendor forever lies in wait about each one of us in all its fullness, but veiled from view, deep down, invisible, far off. It is there, though, not hostile, not reluctant, not deaf. If you summon it by the right word, by its right name, it will come.
> —Franz Kafka

Wellness has a certain abstraction about it; moving in mysterious but rejuvenating energy fields is the hopeful terminus for our immersion in the world of mathematics. A lot of our meandering rivers of wonder and joy spill out into the calming sea of wellness. I guess we are at that mouth figuratively now.

A FLOWER IN THE ABYSS

Whether we be teachers or students, we must reclaim this world, ravaged by the twentieth-century stress around performance and twenty-first-century racial strife, all simmering in the taxing anxiety of an uncertain future for our planet. This is the abyss. How and to what degree we acknowledge its effect on what happens every day in our math classrooms is up to us. If we keep our focus on our students and their well-being, shielding them from the math trauma they believe must await them, then we have a fighting chance. It will start with each one of us individually.

The pandemic still has an unfinished story. Regardless, the long-term effects of it on just about everything will last throughout this decade and beyond. What has emerged from this parched world created by a confluence of social, health, and environmental emergencies are larger conversations around what is now the most important thing in education: humanization.

In late 2020, the *New York Times* started running an opinion series called Let's Start Over. It featured experts in thirteen fields of interest— politics, feminism, work, friendships, conversation, sex, sports, travel, food, literature, fashion, cities, and education. The person who wrote the piece on education was Dr. Jal Mehta, a professor at the Harvard Graduate School of Education, where he studies how to transition from rote learning to deep engagement. His December 2020 article was called "Make Schools More Human."

What Mehta is generally saying isn't terribly new. It's been said by some of the greatest minds in math and education, like Bertrand Russell and Alfred North Whitehead, for almost a hundred years. But what is new is the global pandemic, which has thrown needed kerosene on age-old, going-nowhere, fatiguing conversations. Mehta is spot-on, but, for me, the most interesting part is what he says about curriculum—which gets to the crux of the matter for mathematics. He whimsically, but correctly, references Marie Kondo, the Japanese organizing expert who shows people how to declutter their homes, leaving only the items that bring them joy. Without even having read the article, you may already have guessed what Mehta wrote. Learning must be joyful, meaningful, and filled with moments of being human— warmth, compassion, empathy, and kindness.

Humanization is all that is left. Mathematics must reclaim it to reimagine it. Wellness is found here and nowhere else, and so is its mythical spring of longevity and youthfulness—the same one that Herodotus spoke of thousands of years ago. Our aging bodies constantly dispute this tale, but our minds, usually the last functioning holdout of our mortality, remind us that getting old should be limited to our physical state.

Being carefree and curious should be more accessible than it is. And yet, everyone who has ever wandered into the lair of mathematics prior to the advent of formal education did so with these two traits of wellness. Many floundered and failed. But it has always been about chasing, not catching.

In 1978, the American rock band Heart released its most critically acclaimed album, *Dog and Butterfly*. The title song was inspired by Ann Wilson, the group's iconic singer, watching her dog hopelessly chase and jump after a butterfly. The dog, grounded to the earth and having no concerns or worries, is simply focused on catching the butterfly. The butterfly, beautiful in its colors and symmetry, is more boundless and will never be caught. This is the world of mathematics and wellness. *We are the dog and the universe of math is the butterfly*. The air that separates us from capturing *all* of its knowledge is the ever-so-light medium that we bounce around in. Mathematics is universally buoyant. Doesn't it make sense that our caravan-travels through it would have a charm and lightness accessible to all, crossing all social, racial, economic, justice, and health lines?

One of the problems I have with mathematics is that it is given such serious and heavy treatment in society. Tack on the needless competition, and it is a small wonder everyone doesn't just bow out in exhaustion. It's because they can't. Current math education is about absorbing the shallowest ideas through pressurized performance. Shakespeare would be in awe of this educational tragedy. Mathematical wellness, while being light, is the gateway to absorbing the deepest ideas of mathematics through captivating confusion. The ebullience one feels in this space of curious possibilities is wellness—in both its simplest and most complex forms. But to be in the flow of mathematics with such latitude of exploration is another sought-after pinnacle of human experience.

> # Without mathematics, there is no freedom.
> ## —Edward Frenkel

Since mathematics explains and governs every micro and macro detail of the goings-on of our universe, being connected to mathematics in such ways is really about balance. As I am writing all of this today, the image below popped up in my Facebook feed as *See Your Memories from 7 Years Ago.*

This was not my coffee. It was Peter Harrison's. *Of course it was.* Peter is a practicing Buddhist. Four months later, I would quit teaching in the classroom. I had lost my center. I didn't know how, where, or when I would find it. I just needed to start that journey at the rather ripe age of forty-nine. While that journey continues, even as I scrawl the final few thousand words of this book, I have found my balance—as Peter's oracular cup of java hinted at all those years ago. Like the yin-yang symbol that floated in that mug, staring *indirectly* at me (probably at an angle of 30 degrees), it's been a messy sum of gain and loss, happiness and sadness, and holding on and letting go. The autobiographical thread of this book has been especially important in attempting to bring home the ambitious idea of mathematical wellness. It is knotted together with everything. Peter—no need for formalities at this point—is as major a character in this story as I have portrayed him to be. When I taught in Switzerland for a year, Peter came and visited me. He came to my year 12 International Baccalaureate honors class at the International School of Lausanne on Lake Geneva. He just sat in the back and observed, knowing that this was my time. He traveled across the Atlantic Ocean, just to be silent and patiently watch. Yeah, we went out for dinner and drank same great scotch later that evening, but he wanted to be on the sidelines in my math classroom. I will never forget that moment.

My mathematical world has been, thankfully, porous to all of this. Mathematics to me feels like the title of an old Genesis song from the spectacular *Selling England by the Pound* album, "I Know What I Like (In Your Wardrobe)." Romanticism is inevitable in mathematics. Don't fight it. Let's open that rusty window to the stage of romance for learning that is critical to the lasting ideas in this book. Not just for our students, but for ourselves as well.

COMMUNICATION BREAKDOWN

(Yes, I chose this heading for the Zeppelin song. Are you even allowed to start a sentence with a parenthesis? Pfft, wrong time to consider convention!) A paragraph earlier, I took a little liberty with mathematics' power. I intimated that it could explain everything. I mean, it sure as hell wants to. But mathematics, while having universality to its laws, is in the end a human construct. It has moments where it fails, and we are left holding a mystery. Linear models, while not perfect, cover a modest bit of ground in explaining the natural phenomena around us. The equations might be complex and cover probabilistic and differential backgrounds, but there is a solid pattern of linearity chugging underneath these models. And, if they can't be expressed exactly, they can be approximated with a degree of confidence with linear equations. However, I did use the word *modest*.

Truth be told, most of the natural phenomena around us are nonlinear, and linear approximations are rendered useless. One of the most famous is the dynamics of the double pendulum. Years ago, I would stare at the unpredictable tracing of the tip of the second arm of this pendulum. It had the same effect as staring at a lava lamp. I think I once let the tracing program run for half the day while staring at the points that the pendulum hadn't gone through—yet. If you haven't seen the double pendulum in action, do yourself a favor and just watch it—you may end up in a meditative trance. Crazy irony. The chaotic mathematical behavior is rather calming. I would recommend going to myphysicslab.com.

While there are some complex trig equations that can model exactly the position of where the pendulum *is*, it is impossible to model where it's *going to be*. This is simply because minor changes of initial conditions are dwarfed by the magnitude of future conditions. It's like the butterfly effect on steroids. Problems like the double pendulum are fascinating because they give a clear example of what limitations are present. Clearly all the information is there. There is nothing missing. Our black hole of understanding all comes down to the equations we have built. Is there a deeper block within our ability to see what might be needed? Even mathematics fails. And that for us—*by now*—should put wind in our sails, as it's what binds everything. Showing students that even mathematics is mortal is an important lesson. There are not too many moments where it shrugs its shoulders and says, "I got nothing," so let's be adamant about sharing that gold doubloon of mathematical breakdown whenever and wherever that happens.

> # Failure is more important than success.
> ## —Tetsuya Miyamoto

It turns out that it is much deeper than that. Happily accepting and absorbing failure in mathematics—and life in general—is key to navigating through all the unknowns that constantly lie in front of us. It's why the word *coddiwomple*—purposeful movement in no particular direction—seems so aligned to happily navigating through math's and life's many poorly lit and foggy terrains. John Keats, the great English poet who is probably best known for "Truth is beauty; beauty is truth," is also known for theorizing the idea of something called *negative capability*—the capacity to rest in the unknown and the unresolved, using it as raw material for creative work.

I almost want to type that again. Keats used this idea to explain how great writers like Shakespeare worked. It's precisely how all great mathematicians work. It's also where we should be. The unknown is not a distress call. It is the medium in which Keats believed we find raw creativity. By association, it is also the medium which I believe governs wellness. Wellness, while sounding fragile, is practically titanium where our health and happiness are concerned. And approaching it with the vigor it deserves takes courage.

PHILOSOPHICAL FUSION

In 2015, Parker Palmer gave a commencement address for the ages at Naropa University in Boulder, Colorado. If mathematics could, it would have given a standing ovation. Naropa University, named after the eleventh-century Buddhist teacher, was founded in 1974 by the Tibetan Buddhist teacher and Oxford University graduate Chögyam Trungpa. The goal was to bridge Western scholarship with the wisdom of Eastern philosophy, and to let those ideas ferment for a hundred years (we are halfway there now) with deep contemplative practice of the academic and experiential learning that would blossom over this time—much like a tree. So, as you can see, the table seems set for a highly inspirational speech. In the words of Maria Popova, who wrote about this address, Palmer is "one of the most luminous and hope-giving minds of our time."

The title of the address was "Six Pillars for Leading a Wholehearted Life." For our purposes, everything that needs to be said with regard to wellness and mathematics was front-loaded in this speech:

> Be reckless with affairs of the heart. What I really mean . . . is
> be passionate, fall madly in love with life. Be passionate

217

about some part of the natural and/or human worlds and take risks on its behalf, no matter how vulnerable they make you. No one ever died saying, "I'm sure glad for the self-centered, self-serving, and self-protective life I lived. Offer yourself to the world—your energies, your gifts, your visions, your heart—with open-hearted generosity. But understand that when you live that way, you will soon learn how little you know and how easy it is to fail.

Mathematics has been the embodiment of recklessness with one's heart. It has asked of us, in Bourdain-like fashion, to take risks and leaps of faith. And the price of all that, in the end, is that failure and the unknown will be your most trusted guides. At this stage, failure shouldn't be seen as an ironic path to wellness. We should be normalizing failure as a critical part of personal success. Failure and moving in shadows pairs well with our successes and lighted paths. We incorrectly try to drag everything into the fluorescent lights of success, confidence, and completion. And, after a while, something like math becomes defined only by this. It's not only wrong, but with evidence everywhere now, it is also unhealthy.

CHECKMATE

The biggest series on Netflix in 2020 was *The Queen's Gambit*. I watched it in its entirety three times, and some of my favorite scenes dozens of times—including the final one where Anya Taylor-Joy's riveting character, Beth Harmon, asserts her affirming independence with a glowing walk on a crisp, wintery Moscow morning. I can't watch that ostensibly simple scene without welling up in tears (turns out so did she every time it was shot). As she walks away from the camera to the final scene, her white coat and white hat become more prominent. She now embodies the most powerful piece in the game. The queen cometh. The queen has arrived. (I actually just shed a tear writing this . . .)

Its global popularity, and the noticeable spike in Google searches for "chess" at the time of its release, was due to the galvanizing humanity the series brought to the game of chess. It unapologetically depicted the searing precision and beauty of chess, while the flawed protagonist battles her own awkwardness for most of the series. Every aspect of the game was offered wholeheartedly—flirting *recklessly with the heart*—to the viewing public. Chess waited a long time for its allure and intellectual sensuality to be given such a spotlight. You know what else has laid in wait with the exact same poetic depth? Mathematics. To be very specific, the emotions of mathematics. Emotions that come from thousands and thousands of years of thematic development, failures, setbacks, and eventual triumphs. That's what we should be drinking and getting piss drunk on—because every person belongs here. Mathematics is music for the masses.

By the end of *The Queen's Gambit*, the fifteen-thousand-year-old Indian game brings peace, equanimity, and happiness to Beth. Her coronation occurs in an unassuming setting surrounded by Russian seniors. As it should be. Wellness is confident, modest, and—*because I want to type it again*—a reckless affair of the heart. In the end, Beth would not be governed by politics or religion in her love of chess. She played for the love of the game and wanted to be with the people who love the game as much as she does. Checkmate. We should play with mathematics with the same feral abandon and love. In the end, the mathematics must stand on its own. If it can't, then we aren't really diving deep into our mathematical world as much as we could. Beth went deep into the strategy and psychology of chess to happily end up in that park full of Russian seniors playing chess. If we mirror the same enthusiasm, we will end up in the mathematical forest that is depicted on the front of this book.

Mathematics has had a relationship with wellness for thousands of years. Math education has had a relationship with anxiety for its much shorter duration. Maybe we should stop and pause on that dysfunctional irony. Our pandemic only highlighted that. Math has never been the culprit. It has always been education. One of the many memorable scenes in *The Queen's Gambit* is when Beth Harmon is angrily reflecting on her first loss to the Russian Vasily Borgov. She is lambasting his game and his moves because they were so "obvious, unimaginative, and bureaucratic"—domineering characteristics shared by, at least, twentieth-century math education. I see so much of myself in Beth; her unvarnished character, with equal moments of self-inflicted plunder and regal resonance, is integral in escorting the humanity into this gripping story.

CRACKED, BROKEN, AND UNSURE

The story of this book began in 1997, three years after I met my future wife. We got married in Santorini, Greece, that year. A wedding that was surprisingly arranged by our hotel owner, Thanasis. A stunning sunset and majestic cliffs frame the memory of that late July evening, close to dusk, with fewer than ten family members and friends around. We are no longer married, but we co-parent in the same dwelling because she has a debilitating disease called ankylosing spondylitis. As lifelong friends now, we both fondly reminisce about that moment. Life is messy and unpredictable. There is beauty to be found in that.

Professionally, my life has also been the double pendulum. Most of my teaching career feels a bit empty, as I never taught with or was given opportunities to teach with the philosophy of this book. But no, I wouldn't go back in time to give my younger self any advice, mainly because this book wouldn't exist! Live fearlessly. Embrace failure. Have no regrets.

But, then again, none of my highlights in the classroom had to do with mathematics. I might have fallen short giving my lessons the color and depth they deserved, sometimes even sacrificing the mathematics and professional assessment obligations—sacrificing them for the well-being of my students. One of my greatest accomplishments as a teacher was that I never sent a student to the office in my entire teaching career. I came close in my final year, when a student started cursing excessively at me in front of the class. The classroom was close to being emotionally unsafe. I then raised my voice—which I rarely did—and told the student to take a "long walk"—with a ten-dollar bill I gave him for a meal he was probably missing. The kids that need the most love will show it in the most unlovable ways.

In the final years of my teaching career, I was only given the weaker courses because of my outspokenness about math education, which had political consequences. They, *the system*, eventually put me in a corner of such retribution and constraint that even my love for my students made my position as a teacher untenable. As we know the story, I threw in the towel. Looking back, I don't think I threw it in because I was afraid of the fight. I threw it in because there *was fighting*—why did teaching mathematics have to become a political wrestling match? I wasn't going to wait around for the answer. I had to turn fifty into the new twenty. I literally started again. And again.

My own flaws, imperfections, and struggles are critical pieces in this book. Any value you hopefully are attaching here is enhanced by my shortcomings, not reduced.

NATURE CALLS

Much of our wellness and wisdom is provided by nature. Our most cherished and mindful moments have come with our deepest experiences with nature—from hills and mountains to tiny creeks and wildflowers. Even the smallest piece of nature often turns into a large slice of symbolism for life's purpose and meaning. Sometimes even making it to the big screen.

While my kids have technically outgrown Pixar films, I haven't. Not sure what it says about me or my kids! So, a few days after Christmas in 2020, I watched the movie *Soul* by myself. I thought that the first five minutes of *Up* would never be rivaled for emotion. Well, eleven years later, a five-minute segment planted near the end of *Soul*, set to the softest and quietest piano, now sits up there as one of the most emotionally gripping moments in Pixar's history. The binding piece is a samara seed—better known as *whirlers, twirlers,* or *'copters.* The whole movie, visually and philosophically, huddles around this little gift of nature. I can report that there were no dry eyes.

Reaching for nature as metaphor is relatable and poignant. We are comforted by nature. Shortly after it was published in 2003, a wonderful book by author Yōko Ogawa titled *The Housekeeper and the Professor* was recommended to me. It is a moving story of a housekeeper and a math professor who, due to a brain injury, lives with only eighty minutes of short-term memory. Some beautiful conversations and insights about math—and yes—our own humanness are found in this story. Ogawa's idea of problem solving in mathematics uses elements from nature:

> Solving a problem for which you know there's an answer is like climbing a mountain with a guide, along a trail someone else has laid. In mathematics, the truth is somewhere out there in a place no one knows, beyond all the beaten paths. And it's not always at the top of the mountain. It might be in a crack on the smoothest cliff or somewhere deep in the valley.

Similarly, the late David W. Henderson, who was professor emeritus of mathematics at Cornell University, and passionate about math education for over fifty years, wrote a note coupling the beauty of nature with learning mathematics. The power of the words is slightly reduced by converting his handwriting to text, but I hope you still feel the warmth and beauty of his words:

> Mathematics is a way of looking at your world. Take charge of it—make it yours. Understand how you see things and see how you understand things. Mathematics can say something about you.

Think of what we are embarking on together as a stroll in the woods. I will show you paths that I have trod and point to what I have seen. I have been there many times before—but oh!—there is much more to see that I have not yet seen. You with your unique vision will point out to me things that I have passed by. Feel free to explore—look under stones—down in hollow stumps. You can look up a straight tree and see the sky—You can find a riverlet of water that if followed will lead to the sea. But just as valuable are the little surprises that spark something inside—a trillium in a spot of sun—a scarlet eft wriggling under a fallen leaf. Do not hurry "to get somewhere"—linger a while—listen—see what's around where you are.

Those words connect us to Henderson, mathematics, and nature. We can easily imagine walking alongside him, regardless of whether we are a seasoned high school teacher with a math degree or first-year elementary teacher with an arts background. There are no hierarchies or academic standings on this hike. So much of the mathematics that has crossed my life has been because of how Ogawa and Henderson see the learning of mathematics—natural.

The essence and simplicity of math's historical attraction has been *to play* and *to puzzle*. And the common, humbling experience—as colors this book—has been *failure*. And if we could mine the thinking, pondering, reassessing, doubting, and daydreaming that has occurred in this feral and fertile space of creativity, we would see they are all connected precursors for mathematical wellness.

Back in 2015, I added to my collection of Ivan Moscovich books with the purchase of his deeply engrossing *The Puzzle Universe: A History of Mathematics in 315 Puzzles*. Moscovich is the author of over forty math puzzle books. My introduction to him was around fifteen years ago with his Mastermind series. The first one I bought was *Perplexing Pattern Problems and Other Puzzles*. I could sit here all day and tell you about all the ones I haven't solved!

The reason I bring up Moscovich is because, with *The Puzzle Universe*, I only read the introduction in 2019—the puzzles always drew me in first. But when I finally read it, I went down an Ivan Moscovich rabbit hole, and it only makes sense that he be one of the final mathematicians I mention in this book. First, here is the passage from that introduction that put an immediate smile on my face and inspired with those words to take us out of this last chapter:

> One of the reasons I am so passionate about games and puzzles is that I believe that they can change the way people think. They make us more inventive, more creative, more artistic and even more human. They allow us to see the world in new ways. They can remind us to have fun, make us healthier and even prolong our lives.

Well, since Ivan Moscovich is still alive and well at the age of ninety-four, I would say that his conjecture has some validity. Moscovich is not only a prolific author in the field of math puzzles, but he is also an artist and an inventor of many games. He is also a Holocaust survivor (*deep breath, Sunil*).

At the age of seventeen, Moscovich was taken from his home in Yugoslavia. He ended up in a total of five concentration camps, including Auschwitz. In his memoir, *The Puzzleman*, he has acknowledged that creativity was a source of inspiration to survive and escape the camps. One of the most remarkable things he has done since his escape was to attend the Nuremberg Toy Show every year since it opened—*in 1950*. The 2021 show, postponed due to COVID-19, would be the first one he would miss.

Sexism. Racism. Imprisonment. Death beds. Suicidal ideation. Concentration camps. As we have seen in this book, mathematics has been near the darkest crevices of life. Its humble offering of the tiniest shards of abstract illumination has been a source of refuge, distraction, comfort, healing, and hope. So much of the material world can be taken away. So much of our freedom can be taken away. So much of our health can be taken away. But the spirit of mathematics survives all. It will also survive the COVID-19 pandemic. And its only form that we can accept—because that is the only form it knows—is one that is buoyantly human.

SAMARA

The book must end. I decided before I started writing that it would be bookended by mathematical ideas about prime numbers. Prime numbers have been a preoccupation of mine ever since I left the classroom. They symbolize a window between the known and unknown world. I always feel like I have front row seats to a tiny mystery of the universe when I learn something new about them. As we know, there seems to be no discernable pattern to prime numbers. Their heartbeat is irregular, and many associated ideas about primes remain unproven. Yet we do know they get rarer and rarer as our numbers get bigger. We in fact have a formula that talks about the frequency of primes as we get further out.

Primes, if given a personality, would be a contradictory blend of charisma, enigma, dysfunctionality, and secretiveness. All of them bashing around fiercely and joyfully. Primes want us to believe that they are truly random and unpredictable. Then they throw us a curveball.

In 2015, Stanford mathematicians Kannan Soundararajan and Robert Lemke Oliver discovered a kind of *conspiracy*—that was the word used in a 2016 *Quanta* magazine article—among prime numbers. They studied the first four hundred billion prime numbers, expecting the ending digits of primes—1, 3, 7, and 9—to occur equally, each 25 percent of the time. That prime numbers should end with these numbers randomly, but equally distributed. That's not what they found. These ending digits don't like to repeat with primes. For example, primes ending with 1 are followed by another prime number ending with 1 just 18.5 percent of the time. The other odd numbers have similar aversions. However, as primes are stretched out toward infinity, this localized pattern disappears, and things become random again. Whew! Turns out, however, prime numbers had *another* curveball to throw at the world in 2018. The person who found this one was not a mathematician. It was a chemist! And it was doozy of a curveball.

The announcement of this quirky discovery was all over the major science websites and publications. One of the headlines, from the esteemed *Quanta Magazine,* read: "A Chemist Shines Light on a Surprising Prime Number Pattern." Even without reading further, one is immediately hooked. How could you not be? A *chemist* discovering a patterning behavior of . . . *numbers*? If any kind of numbers were going to get truly weird on us, it was going to be primes, right?

It turns out that prime numbers have quasi-crystal-like structure! Umm . . . primes are numbers, not shapes? Well, not related, but square numbers, cubic numbers, triangular numbers, etc. have a geometry to them. But primes, being the poster children for randomness, would hardly seem like candidates to have any shape or form attached to them. But I suppose the quirkiness of primes invites a quirkiness of examination. Specifically, from the Princeton University *chemist,* Salvatore Torquato.

It's quite common for chemists, in order to better understand the nature of matter, to shoot X-rays at things and analyze the diffraction that results from all these rays bouncing off the atoms. The practice has been around for over a hundred years. What Torquato did was simply follow a hunch. He wondered if prime numbers had a similar structure, and, if so, whether it could be exposed by a similar experiment. Sure enough, he took exceptionally long sequences of prime numbers (about a million) starting at very large numbers and modeled them as one long string of particles. He then shot virtual X-rays at them. The result was a structure remarkably like quasi crystals! As such, that is why I asked the designer to put a crystal in the distance of the book cover. It was the symbolic end for this book.

Primes continue to unravel their mysterious beauty to us. Will there be implications for this in terms of encryption safety (very large primes are used in securing financial transactions)? Who knows? This is all but one (cue reference to Stanley Kramer's 1963 comedy) *very, very, very, very* tiny piece of the mosaic of mathematics. It is simply one of millions of whirling samaras available to us. And the expression that we should wear as they fall into our lives is nothing short of the one that jazz musician Joe Gardner has—when a samara seed spirals down into his hand from an autumn maple in New York. The creators of *Soul* were keenly aware of the emotional potential of something so ordinary and small. In mathematics, it is equally as transcending.

This book is just one more *samara seed*. However, it might be the first book that has made that self-reference. Staying small to inspire big. Then, the way I would like to think of myself as an author here is like a gas station owner giving all of you a full tank of *curiosity gas*. There are many other similar gas stations. You just happened to stop at mine. Thank you.

I hope, as well, that you enjoy the *road snacks* of problems and puzzles presented in this book. I have marked *but a few landmarks* of mathematicians and their stories. You will surely find many more along the way. More than anything, I hope I have given you a guide to find the healthiest ideas about mathematics so that your journey, with a charmingly unpredictable compass in hand, always guides your experiences toward communal awe and wonder.

Curiosity will take you further along the mathematical roads than anything else. Sometimes you will be stuck in traffic. Sometimes you will be lost on some country back trail. Sometimes you may slide off the road entirely. *Stillness, lostness, and failure.* The best rewards for pursuing mathematics. And even though you never run out of curiosity, don't be bothered about planning your trip or arriving somewhere on time. You will quickly realize there are no itineraries to complete, and you can't be late. Sorry, Rabbit. Mathematics doesn't own an agenda planner or watch. Neither should you. Just know that wellness is a travel companion you will soon encounter in your chasing adventures in the wilderness of mathematics. And as with any road trip, you will need good music. If I can select an appropriate first song, it would be "Born to Go" by the psychedelic, space-rock band Hawkwind. Crank it up. Crank up the math. Crank up your life—every minute of it! Allow the light of mathematics to reflect, refract, and mingle warmly within the prism that is you.

Go!

> **Wilderness is not a luxury, but a necessity of the human spirit.**
> **—Edward Abbey**

ACKNOWLEDGMENTS

Since this book is a personal, mathematical story—still unfinished—anyone who has listened to any part of it and/or has shared their own story and reflections about this subject must be acknowledged in some fashion. Peter Harrison is someone I owe much of this book to. He was there at the beginning of my story and was an integral part in shaping it and giving it much-needed color. James Tanton for being a wealth of mathematical knowledge, guidance, and joy the last five years. Buzzmath, the first company that hired me after I left teaching and my math business burned down. They gave me the opportunity to travel to math conferences all over North America and meet hundreds of kindred spirits who kept inspiring me with their wisdom and friendship. Their collective energy is housed warmly in this book. To the thousands of students that I have taught. Your myriad of personalities and experiences are tattooed on me forever and have always been a motivational source of my writings. And there is a special circle of friends that I have known for twenty-five years through the most Canadian of things—hockey pools. Their kindness and support of my writing have always been a place of grounded appreciation. Thanks, Multi. My publishing and editing team. It goes without saying that this book could not exist without them. But the passion and professionalism that went into producing this math book was extraordinary. To George and Paige Couros for having the belief in the power of my writing ability and inviting me to join IMPress Books. To my sadly departed heroes of truth, living on the edge, and kindness, Anthony Bourdain and Lemmy. I could not have told these stories with comfort and boldness without the extraordinary influence your art had on me.

Since this is my last math book, it is only fitting to acknowledge family. My parents, sister, brother, nieces, and nephews. We celebrate this milestone together.

Lastly, to my children, Aidan and Raya. I love you the size of Graham's number. May you inherit some parts of this book when you are older—and chase your own rabbits of life's curiosity and wonder.

ABOUT SUNIL SINGH

Sunil Singh is a well-known and highly respected leader in the emergent area of mathematical storytelling. He has given several keynotes and dozens of presentations and webinars on this topic with major math organizations like National Council of Teachers of Mathematics (NCTM), National Council of Supervisors of Mathematics (NCSM), and United States National Commission on Mathematical Instruction (USNC/  MI). He is also the author of *Pi of Life: The Hidden Happiness of Mathematics* and the coauthor of *Math Recess: Playful Learning in an Age of Disruption*. He taught math, physics, and occasionally English, for nineteen years before embarking on a new journey of sharing his passion for math history and narrative with people all around the world. He works as a program advisor at Amplify to promote rich storytelling, something that he helped build into their K to 12 math platform, and at Mathigon as a content writer. He has also given workshops at the Museum of Mathematics in New York and the Royal Conservatory of Music in Toronto. In his free time, he serves as the president of the board of directors at the Human Restoration Project, a nonprofit initiative to make schools more human, and is part of Mathigon's Education Advisory Group. He lives in Toronto, Ontario, where he cheers for every Toronto sports team *except* the Maple Leafs. He can be followed on Twitter at @Mathgarden or reached by email at chasingrabbits2021@gmail.com.

MORE BOOKS FROM

IMPRESS

Empower: What Happens when Students Own Their Learning
by A.J. Juliani and John Spencer

*Learner-Centered Innovation: Spark Curiosity,
Ignite Passion, and Unleash Genius*
by Katie Martin

*Unleash Talent: Bringing Out the Best in Yourself
and the Learners You Serve*
by Kara Knollmeyer

*Reclaiming Our Calling: Hold On to the Heart,
Mind, and Hope of Education*
by Brad Gustafson

Take the L.E.A.P.: Ignite a Culture of Innovation
by Elisabeth Bostwick

*Drawn to Teach: An Illustrated Guide to
Transforming Your Teaching written*
by Josh Stumpenhorst and illustrated by Trevor Guthke

Math Recess: Playful Learning in an Age of Disruption
by Sunil Singh and Dr. Christopher Brownell

*Innovate inside the Box: Empowering Learners
Through UDL and Innovator's Mindset*
by George Couros and Katie Novak

*Personal & Authentic: Designing Learning
Experiences That Last a Lifetime*
by Thomas C. Murray

*Learner-Centered Leadership: A Blueprint for Transformational
Change in Learning Communities*
by Devin Vodicka

*Kids These Days: A Game Plan for (Re)Connecting
with Those We Teach, Lead, & Love*
by Dr. Jody Carrington

*UDL and Blended Learning: Thriving in Flexi*ble Learning Landscapes
by Katie Novak and Catlin Tucker

*Teachers These Da*ys: Stories & Strategies for Reconnection
by Dr. Jody Carrington and Laurie McIntosh

*Because of a Teacher: Stories of the Past to Inspire the
Future of Education written and curated*
by George Couros

Evolving Education: Shifting to a Learner-Centered Paradigm
by Katie Martin